WOODWORK

TWO

DAVID M. WILLACY B ED DLC

Head of Art Studies, St. Albans School, St. Albans
Moderator and Chief Examiner in Woodwork, GCE and CSE Boards

Illustrated with photographs
and with line drawings by
NORMA CROCKFORD

SECOND EDITION

NELSON

Thomas Nelson and Sons Ltd
Nelson House Mayfield Road
Walton-on-Thames Surrey KT12 5PL
P.O. Box 18123 Nairobi Kenya
Watson Estate Block A 13 Floor
Watson Road Causeway Bay Hong Kong
116-D JTC Factory Building
Lorong 3 Geylang Square Singapore 14

Thomas Nelson Australia Pty Ltd
19—39 Jeffcott Street West Melbourne Victoria 3003

Thomas Nelson and Sons (Canada) Ltd
81 Curlew Drive Don Mills Ontario

Thomas Nelson (Nigeria) Ltd
8 Ilupeju Bypass PMB 21303 Ikeja Lagos

First published in 1972
Reprinted three times
Second edition 1980

ISBN 0 17 431026 9

NCN 3175 28 0

By the same author
WOODWORK ONE

CONTENTS

GENERAL ACKNOWLEDGEMENTS

The author and publishers are grateful to the following for permission to reproduce photographs on the pages listed below. Those photographs not acknowledged are by the author.

Arenson International Ltd. / 83
BC Plywood Ltd. / 178
Beaver and Tapley Ltd. / 60
Benchairs Ltd. / 130 (right)
Ciba-Geigy (UK) Ltd. / 128
CIMCO Ltd. / 138
Cintride Ltd. / 119, 177 (left)
Copydex Ltd. / 179 (bottom)
Craft Supplies / 121
Cubestore / 11
Denford Tools Ltd. / 100 (bottom)
Flexitools Ltd. / 129, 130 (left)
Formica Ltd. / 176
Fritzhausen-Mobler Ltd. / 90
GKN Ltd. / 62
E. Gomme Ltd. / 53
Habitat Ltd. / 78 (top), 94, 133 (bottom)
Hille Ltd. / 76 (top), 87
Kiddicraft Ltd. / 88
Lucas Furniture Ltd. / 81 (right)
Mann Bros. Ltd. / 80
Henry Moore Esq., O.M., C.H. / 153
James Neill & Co. Ltd. / 177 (right)
OMK Design Ltd. / 76 (bottom)
Paramo Ltd. / 179 (top)
Pirelli Ltd. / 130
Race Furniture Ltd. / 133 (top)
The Rawlplug Co. Ltd. / 148
Record Ridgway Ltd. / 22, 118, 122, 181
The Royal Academy of Arts / 154
Gordon Russell Ltd. / 77, 78 (bottom)
Ryderglyde Ltd. / 168 (bottom)
Safety Products Ltd. / 95
John Spielman Esq. / 158
Stanley Tools Ltd. / 17, 59 (right), 106, 109, 112, 151 (bottom), 152
Tate Gallery / 157 (left)
The Victoria and Albert Museum / 42, 75, 117
Wadkin Ltd. / 96, 97, 102, 103

AUTHOR'S ACKNOWLEDGEMENTS

I am very grateful for the help given in compiling this book by the following firms and organisations: Aaronson Brothers, Aeropreen, 'Alwayse' Castor Co., Armstrong Patents Co., Berman Brothers, The British Standards Institution, Carborundum Co., Carver & Co., Ciba-Geigy (UK), Cintride, James Collins, Copydex, Crompton Nettlefold Stenman, Cuprinol, Denford Machine Tools, Dunlop, English Abrasives Corporation, English Sewing, Evode, The Fibre Building Board Development Organisation, Firth Brown Tools, Fitchett and Woollacott, Formica, Furniglas, Gliksten Hardwoods, Guest Keen & Nettlefold, Hadfields (Merton), L. G. Harris & Co., T. S. Harrison & Sons, W. W. Hill Son & Wallace, Imperial Chemical Industries, F. Leiner and Co., Isaac Lord, The 3M Co., Record Ridgway Marples, James Neill and Co. (Eclipse), Nettlefold Stenman, Norton Abrasives, F. Parramore & Sons, E. Parsons & Sons, Power Tools, Pirelli, Plywood Manufacturers Association of British Columbia, Rabone Chesterman, The Rawlplug Co., Rentokil, Rexel; Wm. Ridgway & Sons, Rustins, Rylands Brothers, Safety Products, Selectus, Spear & Jackson, Stanley-Bridges, Stanley Tools, Storey Brothers and Co., Sterling Roncraft, Timber Research & Development Association, UAC Timber, Alec Tiranti, Thor Hammer Co., Tower Manufacturing Co., Unibond, Wadkin, Wolf Electric Tools, E. C. Young.

My thanks go also to Mr. D. J. Gothard and Mr. S. F. Robertson who took the photographs in the design section and those of the tools in workshop use.

D.M.W.

QUESTION ACKNOWLEDGEMENTS

After each chapter of the book there is a selection of questions which should be useful and which will help students to prepare for theory and design examinations.

The type of question asked differs from one region to another but most of these 'styles' are covered by long and short questions taken from a variety of examining boards' recent papers.

Almost all the information needed to answer these questions is to be found in this book but occasionally it will be necessary to consult specialist books, e.g. on lathework.

I am grateful to the Boards listed below for the permission given to reprint questions from their examination papers.

Initial letters are used in the text as follows to indicate the Board concerned. Where no initials appear the questions are from other sources.

EM   East Midland Regional Examination Board
MET   Metropolitan Regional Examination Board
NW   North Western Secondary Schools Examination Board
SE   South East Regional Examination Board
S   Southern Regional Examination Board
W   Welsh Joint Education Committee
WM   West Midlands Examination Board
AEB   Associated Examining Board for the General Certificate of Education
JMB   Northern Universities Joint Matriculation Board

INTRODUCTION

TO THE TEACHER

The contents of the first four chapters of this book clearly describe the main constructions and methods of joining wood together. The information is presented in a series of twenty-four sections which follow on from *Woodwork 1*.

The notes which accompany the many illustrations may often mention workshop practices but the demonstration of marking-out and cutting various joints can only be done effectively by you.

The sections on TURNING, LAMINATING AND BENDING, UPHOLSTERY, and WOOD CARVING AND SCULPTURE are simplified and are only intended as introductions to subjects requiring further study.

There is a full guide to furniture 'hardware' and attention is drawn to the safety and correct use of machine tools. Some of the 'new' materials, tools and processes included in Chapter 12 may have already found a regular and useful place in your practical work. In time some of them will become an integral part of the theory of workshop practice.

The NOTES TO STUDENTS give suggestions for project work but it is hoped that students will also have their own ideas for these projects.

TO THE STUDENT

The clear drawings and concise notes in the chapters on CONSTRUCTIONS AND JOINTS should present you with enough information to plan your practical work.

The DESIGN section may suggest ideas that can be adapted for your own jobs and the chapters on TURNING, UPHOLSTERY and WOOD CARVING AND SCULPTURE may encourage you to read more extensively on each subject and to produce useful and exciting work of your own.

You will gain a basic knowledge of machine tools by working through that chapter and particular attention should be paid to the notes on safety, before using a machine for the first time.

If you are required to produce a study or a project for your examination, the last chapter will be of benefit. Manufacturers and organisations are only too willing to help you by supplying information, provided that such information is requested along the lines suggested.

CONSTRUCTIONS AND JOINTS

GENERAL INTRODUCTION

Each woodworker, irrespective of the level at which he practises his craft, is dealing with a common material, although the treatment it receives may be quite different.

The carver soon knows the working qualities of his block of Yew or Mahogany, and which tools are the most efficient for the job. The canoe-builder, working to set plans, uses different techniques. He has to cut man-made sheets of plywood, stitch them together with copper wire and finally join them with glass fibre and resin.

The woodworker learns that a traditional construction with dovetailing makes a very strong box and that, by contrast, MR adhesive and oval wire nails are adequate for building a garden cold frame. Each craftsman discovers, through experience, the quality and usefulness of the timbers that are available and the many ways in which they may be joined together.

CONSTRUCTIONS

Over the centuries four main types of construction have developed:

1. **The Box or Carcase**
2. **The Stool or Table**
3. **The Frame and Panel**
4. **The Slab (large, flat surfaces).**

More recent developments in, and the uses of, man-made materials and special fittings have resulted in the partial elimination of many traditional methods of construction.

The bedside cabinet illustrated shows three main types of traditional construction used in one piece of furniture—carcase, stool, and frame and panel constructions.

By contrast, the low table is a fine example of slab construction. It is made entirely from a sheet of chipboard.

Slab constructions of man-made board first began to replace the frame and panel construction of doors because of their flatness and stability.

Traditional constructions used in a bedside cabinet

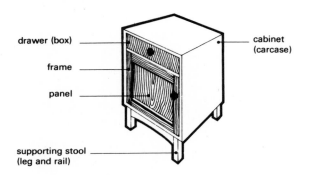

drawer (box)
frame
panel
cabinet (carcase)
supporting stool (leg and rail)

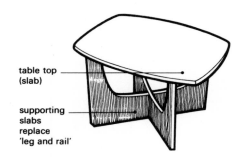

table top (slab)
supporting slabs replace 'leg and rail'

JOINTS

The traditional 'laws' covering how a piece of wood should be joined in making furniture have changed considerably since the introduction of modern adhesives and furniture fittings. The principles, however, have remained the same. The joint must be strong enough to do its job efficiently and, if it is visible, it should be neat and attractive to look at.

There are many methods of joining the same two pieces of wood together. Each method is the result of ideas that generations of craftsmen have developed.

In choosing a method for joining, five points should be borne in mind:

1. The strength of the joint required.
2. The type and size of the material being used.
3. The article being made.
4. The skill that you as a craftsman possess.
5. The machinery available to give you help.

For example, while you may not be skilful in using a chisel, your knowledge of how to set up and operate a mortising attachment on a pillar drill will enable you to make more effective joints in this way.

Metal and plastic joints may be used to joint machine prepared material but these require either the skill to design them or the skill of selecting them from those available.

The following sections describe the main types of joints and how they are used with the four different constructions mentioned.

The Cubestore storage system uses Softboard slabs inserted into extruded aluminium corner pieces.

BOX OR CARCASE CONSTRUCTIONS

1

37 CORNER JOINTS 1

THE BUTT JOINT

This is the simplest form of corner joint and is used in box constructions, where the components are butted together.

The joint is prepared by planing the ends square, often on a shooting board, or sawing almost to length and trimming on a disc sander. (See *Chapter 6 p. 100.*)

A combination of dovetail nailing (see *Woodwork 1 p. 95*) and a synthetic resin adhesive makes a suitable joint for external softwood jobs, such as garden frames and seed-boxes. Screws may also be used but are not so effective in end grain.

Additional strength for the joint may be gained by gluing triangular corner blocks into the corners.

THE REBATED OR LAPPED JOINT

The rebated or lapped joint withstands outside pressures better than the butt joint. Panel pins are also often used as well as adhesives. These are punched below the surface and the resulting holes suitably filled.

In order to make the joint, square off the side of the box and mark out a rebate on the end. The rebate should be equal to the thickness of the side and between half and two-thirds the thickness of the end.

This joint can also be grooved to half thickness in order to fit a base, where the groove does not have to be specially concealed. It is used in simple drawer constructions.

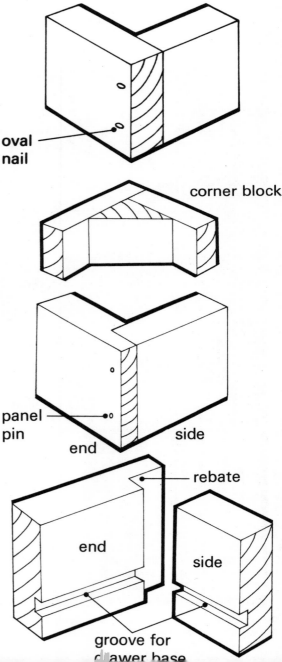

oval nail

corner block

panel pin

end

side

rebate

end

side

groove for drawer base

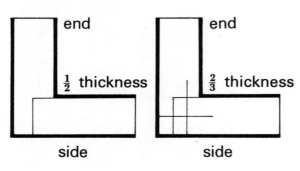

end

$\frac{1}{2}$ thickness

side

end

$\frac{2}{3}$ thickness

side

THE TONGUED AND GROOVED JOINT

This is stronger than either the butt or lapped joint and resists both internal and external pressures.

The side is usually rebated to half its thickness and the end is grooved to accommodate the tongue which is formed from the side.

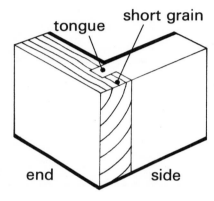

This joint gains its strength from having a large gluing surface. A disadvantage, however, is that all the end grain shows and the short grain is liable to break out, although this is not a problem in the common stair construction, where the joint is most often used.

Grooved stair 'tread'

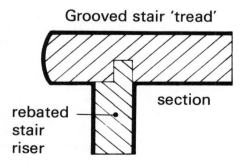

The tongued and grooved joint is also found in simple drawer construction, especially in white-wood furniture, when the drawer front overlaps the surrounding carcase or framework.

THE FINGER OR COMB JOINT

This joint was originally devised and used 'dry' for the rails of gate-leg tables, so that they could pivot along their length and support the table flaps. Nowadays this job is usually done with special metal or nylon fittings.

The finger joint used as a corner joint is simple to make since it has no sloping angles. Because of the large gluing surfaces, it is also very strong.

It is particularly useful for making corner joints on boxes of thin material, as the joint can be cut by using a circular saw with the appropriate jig attachment or guides.

Example: hand-cut joint

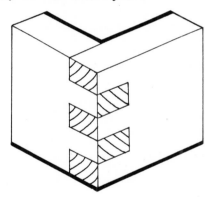

Example: machine-cut finger joint on thin box sides 6 to 9 mm thick

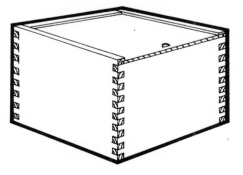

38 CORNER JOINTS 2

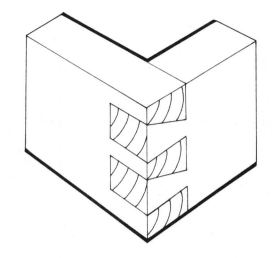

THE THROUGH OR COMMON DOVETAIL

Dovetailing is the strongest method of joining together the corners of wide boards when using solid timber. In the furniture industry their use is diminishing with the extensive employment of man-made boards and the neat fixing devices described in Chapter 11. Where wide boards of solid timber are still used, they are made with matching cutters on a machine, and the pins and tails are the same size.

However, the joint with pins and tails of equal size is often unnecessarily strong for the job it has to do. Thus the craftsman can afford to weaken it slightly, but improve its appearance, by making the tails larger than the pins.

An approximate guide for calculating the proportions of the hand-made joint is that the base of the pins should be equal to the thickness of the material and there should be one tail for every 25 mm of depth, e.g. a box which is 75 mm deep should have three tails—see illustration.

Although larger work will require comparatively fewer tails, there is a tendency for wide boards to warp at the edges. To prevent this, two small extra dovetails are often used.

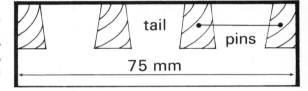

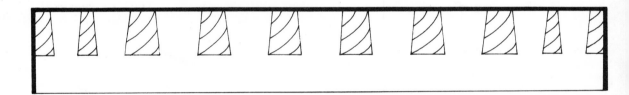

HARDWOODS AND SOFTWOODS

When in any doubt make the narrowest part of the pins in hardwood about 6 mm wide and in softwood about 9 mm wide. The slope of the dovetails can vary between 1 in 8 for hardwoods and 1 in 6 for softwoods. They should be marked out with a template.

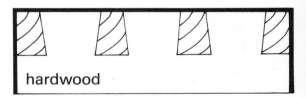

hardwood

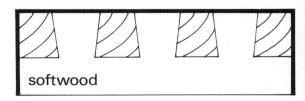

softwood

THE LIDDED BOX

When a box has a hinged lid, a perfect fit can be ensured by making the lid and the base together and sawing off between the gauged lines. The lid must include a full tail, and an extra wide pin is used to allow for the saw cut and for truing up the surfaces with a plane.

THE DOVETAIL JOINT ADAPTED FOR GROOVES AND REBATES

Grooves and rebates in through dovetails must be allowed for when planning the joints. Two of several methods are shown and in each instance the groove or rebate must be cut before marking out and cutting the joint.

The groove can be cut to its finished depth (usually one half the thickness of the side) and the bottom dovetail is cut accordingly. The distance of the groove from the bottom edge must be more than the width of the base of the pin.

When rebating, the common error of a gap can be avoided by allowing a projection on the end shoulder of the tail piece, equal in length to the width of the rebate. This projection is sometimes referred to as a cog.

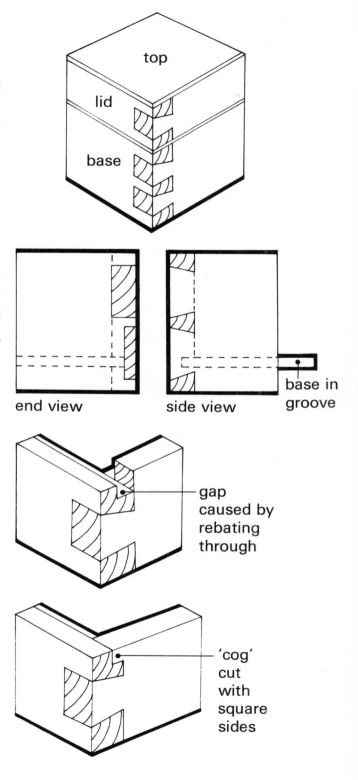

top

lid

base

end view

side view

base in groove

gap caused by rebating through

'cog' cut with square sides

THE LAPPED DOVETAIL

This joint has been devised so that end grain shows only on one surface. It is used mainly at the corners of drawer fronts and for the bottoms of solid wood carcases, or where a false top is needed. (See *Section 41*)

The large gluing surface of the joint gives it maximum strength.

The drawer front is invariably thicker than the sides and the lap is generally made 3-6 mm thick.
Note: The lap must be supported when being cut with a chisel, as it can easily 'break-out'.

The proportion of tails to pins is the same as for the through dovetail joint.

One advantage of the lapped dovetail is that, if carefully positioned, a groove for the drawer bottom can be ploughed, without adapting the joint and without it being visible from the outside.

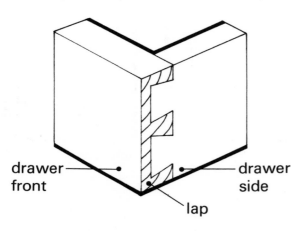

drawer front — drawer side — lap

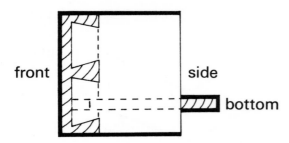

front   side   bottom

39   SIDE JOINTS

The carcase or box joints described so far are used when joining the sides to a top or base and are, therefore, corner joints. Large cabinets, however, such as sideboards, have partitions; bookcases have a number of fixed shelves, and other boxes may be divided into numerous compartments. These additions to the cabinet involve the use of side joints which give strength and support to the main box.

These side joints are usually grooves which are cut across the width of the outsides and are called housings.

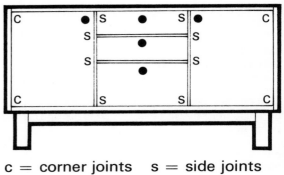

c = corner joints   s = side joints

THE THROUGH HOUSING

This is the simplest way of making the side joint. The groove is first sawn across and the bulk of the waste is removed with a chisel. The groove is then levelled with a router plane. (See *Woodwork 1, p. 112.*)

The depth of the housing is commonly one-third the thickness of the material. In order to obtain a good fit, the shelf or partition must be finished to size before marking out.
Note: This is unnecessary with pre-finished boards, e.g. veneered chipboard.

Although the joint is normally only glued, some softwood jobs, such as step ladders, are strengthened by using nails.

THE STOPPED HOUSING

More care is required to cut the stopped housing but it has the advantage of not showing the joint on the front edge. It gives a neater and more desirable finish for most work.

The housing should not be stopped too far from the front edge otherwise a solid shelf may tend to 'curl' or warp. A stop of 9-12 mm is adequate for most jobs.

AVOIDING A GAP

In making both through and stopped housings you may have difficulty in avoiding a gap.

One way of overcoming such an error in shelf-making is to saw a small shoulder on the top edge of the shelf equal to the depth of the housing and about 3 mm wide.

The corresponding housing should be cut accordingly and any adjustments made with a finely-set plane.

through housing

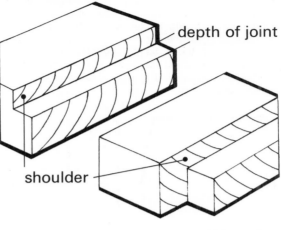

depth of joint

shoulder

stopped housing

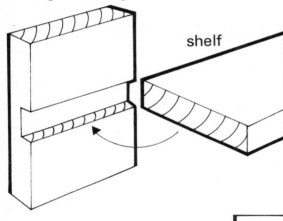

shelf

through housing

through housing
stopped housing

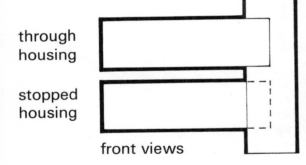

front views

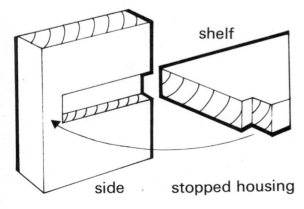

shelf

side   stopped housing

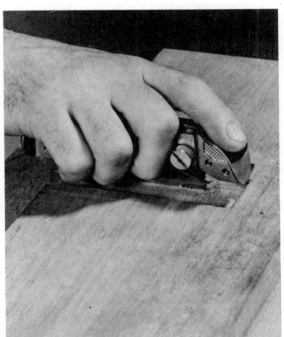

A side-rebate plane being used to trim the side of a stopped housing.

17

THE DOVETAIL HOUSING

The sides of very large cabinets often tend to bow outwards unless the material from which they are made is very thick and therefore heavy and ugly in appearance. Bowing can be avoided by using a dovetailed housing which will resist a sideways pull. This joint, however, has to be inserted after the main carcase has been glued up and it is therefore difficult to make a joint which is tight enough and yet will slide across.

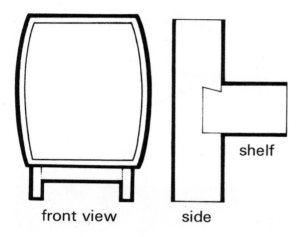

front view   side

To cut the housing accurately it is best to use a saw-guide planed to the correct dovetail angle and this can be held down with a G-cramp. The dovetail on the shelf can be cut by preparing a rebate in the usual way and then trimming to the required angle with a large chisel, making final adjustments with a side-rebate plane.

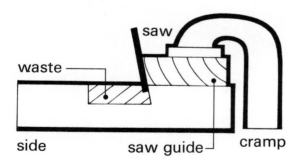

HOUSING WITH TENONS

A fairly common feature of hand-made cabinets is the use of fixed shelving. The shelf is joined to the sides with a housing and tenons. The tenons may be stopped and are therefore invisible, or they may be brought through. They are more often brought through because they are stronger and can be wedged, sometimes in a decorative manner, using wedges of a contrasting timber, e.g. sycamore and walnut, or oak and rosewood.

MAKING THE TENONS

Tenons and their corresponding mortises are marked out with a mortise gauge. (See *Woodwork 1, p. 44.*) The tenons are accurately cut, first down the grain and then across the shoulders with a backsaw. (See *Woodwork 1, p. 59.*)

The mortises are chopped out with a mortise chisel of the correct width. The blade is used across the grain and then across the shoulders with a backsaw. the chisel is hit with a mallet.

The preparation of wedges is described in Section 47.

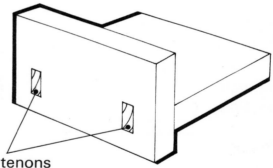

tenons
placed near edge
of shelf to offset tendency
to warp

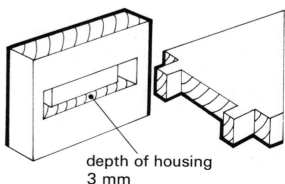

depth of housing
3 mm

VERTICAL PARTITIONS

These are usually fixed in one of two ways depending on the strength required. Either through or stopped housings can be used, or pinned mortise and tenon joints.

With the latter method, the tenons are often brought through the outside carcase and wedged for extra strength. This can be done where the top of a box is to have a false top and the joint will not be seen, or where the bottom of a cabinet has to take an excessive load, e.g. in a large wall cupboard.

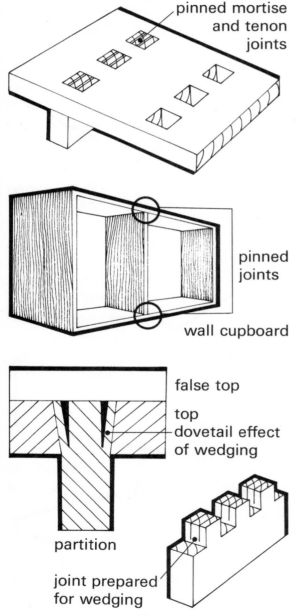

pinned mortise and tenon joints

pinned joints

wall cupboard

false top

top

dovetail effect of wedging

partition

joint prepared for wedging

40 EDGE JOINTS

Manufactured boarding, such as plywood, block-board and chipboard, can be made in large widths. This is one reason why it is nearly always used for large items of furniture, e.g. sideboards and wardrobes.

Where such jobs are hand-made, solid timber is occasionally used. Because only a few types of timber are available in wide boards e.g. African Mahogany or Japanese Elm, a number of narrower boards normally 150 – 200 mm wide have to be joined together. This is called edge jointing. There are four methods of edge jointing in common use:

    Butt jointing
    Dowelling
    Loose tongue and groove
    Tongue and groove

THE BUTT JOINT

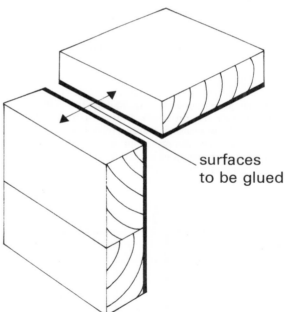

surfaces to be glued

This is the basic joint which relies for its strength on close-fitting surfaces and a suitable adhesive.

Before planing, the direction of the surface grain should be noted with an arrow in order to make later cleaning up easier. The edges of the boards must first be planed with a try plane. After planing, the position of each board should be labelled to assist the process of gluing up. The adhesive is then applied to the edges and the boards are sash-cramped together. (See page 67).

In order to keep the finished board flat, it is advisable to alternate the heart sides of adjacent boards.

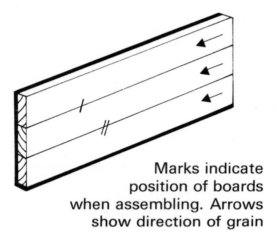

Marks indicate position of boards when assembling. Arrows show direction of grain

When joining boards edge to edge much thought is needed from the initial selection of the timber through to the final assembly. Match strongly-grained wood where possible. Curved grain should be related as in sketch A and not as in sketch B.
Note: This is not important when joining softwoods that will be painted.

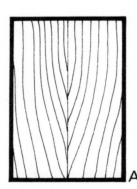

A   B

THE DOWELLED JOINT

This common joint has the same external appearance as the butt joint but, because of the hardwood dowels, it has considerably more strength. The joint is mainly used when the thickness of the boards exceeds 12 mm.

The dowels are often in pairs and can be marked out by using a try square and marking gauge, or by using a jig.

Simple jigs can be made in the workshop from short ends of timber, or a metal dowelling jig can be used. (See *Woodwork 1, p. 88*.) A metal precision tool will ensure a degree of accuracy not easily attained in any other way.

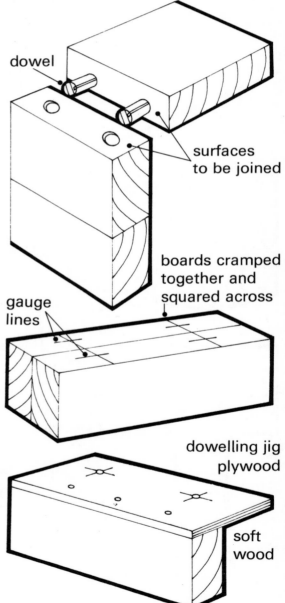

dowel

surfaces to be joined

boards cramped together and squared across

gauge lines

dowelling jig plywood

soft wood

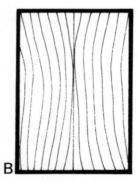

THE DOWEL

The length of the dowels will depend upon what they will be used to join. Both ends should be 'coned' off, with a dowel bit or by rubbing them on glasspaper at an angle. This coning allows the dowel to be driven in easily.

A groove cut along the length of the dowel will enable any surplus glue to be forced out, thus preventing splitting. This groove can be sawn, or made by driving the rod through a dowel plate.

Tight-fitting joints can be glued with a PVA adhesive, (see *Woodwork 1, p. 90*) but where any slackness occurs a resin glue is recommended.
Note: Make certain that the glue is spread evenly around the hole and not just at the bottom—a common fault.

coning

groove

light countersink
to prevent
build-up of glue

shank of dowel
bit fits in
brace chuck

dowel plate

THE LOOSE TONGUE AND GROOVE

This strong joint is easy to prepare either by hand or machine.

After careful planing of the edge of the boards, grooves may be cut with a plough plane (see *Woodwork 1, p. 116*) or with a suitable circular saw blade.

A plywood fillet is commonly employed and in order to ensure a tight fit, standard metric blades are available for use with the plough plane.

Alternatively, a hardwood fillet may be prepared. The grain should run across its width so that it is cross-grained.

Grooves should be made about one-third the thickness of the material. On thick boards of over 25 mm two fillets may be used.

The large gluing surface ensures considerable strength but a disadvantage is that the joint is visible on end grain.

cross-
grained
hardwood fillet

Two plywood fillets
used on thick boards

21

THE TONGUED AND GROOVED JOINT

The tongued and grooved joint lacks the strength of the loose tongue joint because it has less gluing surface. To ensure a good joint a pair of matching cutters should be used in the plough plane. The single blade cuts the groove and the forked blade cuts the shoulders at either side of the remaining tongue.

SMALL BOXES

When small boxes are made from softwoods, the joints employed usually depend upon the purpose and expected life of the box. For example, seed boxes are constructed fairly crudely with nails or staples, whereas storage boxes for electrical components would be made more carefully, using a lapped joint.

Jewellery or glove boxes fashioned from carefully selected pieces of hardwood, such as Rosewood, Walnut, or Mahogany, would normally have delicately proportioned dovetails exhibiting the skill of the craftsman who made them.

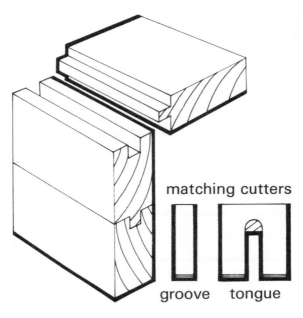

matching cutters

groove   tongue

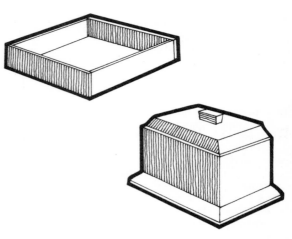

Plough plane used to cut groove.

Necklace box made from cedarwood.

LARGE BOXES

In the illustration showing a cabinet, lapped dovetails, that cannot generally be seen, are used on all corner joints. The false top is slot-screwed on, thus allowing for the movement that is possible with any solid timber.

The plinth may be made using any of the corner joints previously illustrated but, if end grain is to be avoided, the corners should be mitred. The mitre can be strengthened by gluing veneer fillets into saw cuts in the joint, or by gluing blocks on the inside corners.

The wall bookcase illustrated would have dovetail joints on the sides to take the weight of its contents. A rebated back may have to be allowed for although this is not a necessity.

A stopped or tapered dovetail housing may be used for fixing the shelf but, as all the corner joints are showing, tenons taken through a housing will not spoil the appearance of the sides.

Long bookcases may need a central shelf support to withstand the downward thrust of the contents.

A writing cabinet is similarly constructed and partitions, probably being of thin material, would be housed in position.

The drawers, which are in fact small boxes within a larger box, are made in the traditional way, in keeping with the design of the cabinet.

Wall bookcase

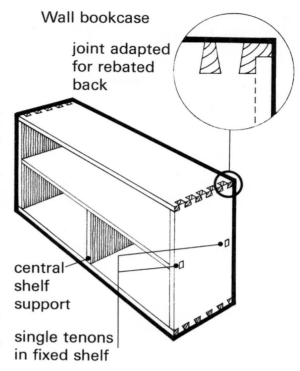

joint adapted for rebated back

central shelf support

single tenons in fixed shelf

Writing cabinet

Cabinet

grooved back

slots for top

housed shelf

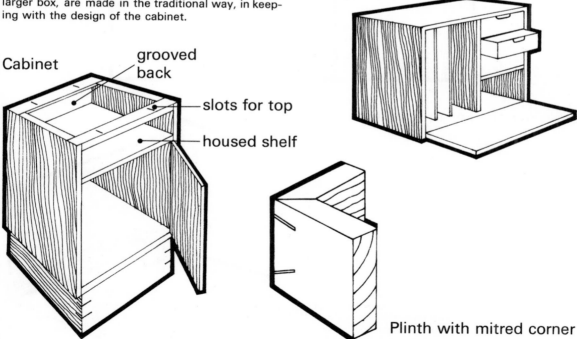

Plinth with mitred corner

42 CONSTRUCTING THE BOX OR CARCASE 2 — DRAWERS

Drawers are boxes that are made to slide in and out of carcases or framed cabinets, or be suspended from table constructions. They can be made in any number of ways, using the corner joints shown in Sections 37 and 38.

A SIMPLE DRAWER

Simple drawer construction is suitable for softwood drawers. The thicker sides can be grooved and the joints both glued and pinned for strength.

A TRADITIONAL DRAWER

The thin drawer sides are lap dovetailed into the thicker front which is grooved to take a solid wood bottom.

The grain of the bottom runs across the width of the drawer. It is rebated to fit the grooved drawer slips and is slot-screwed to the back to allow for any shrinkage or expansion. The drawer slips strengthen the thin sides and increase their running surface.

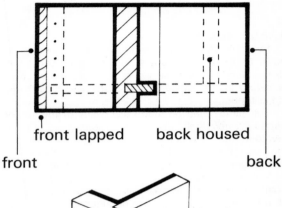

front lapped   back housed

front   back

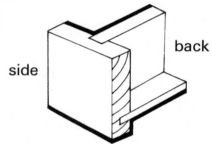

side   back

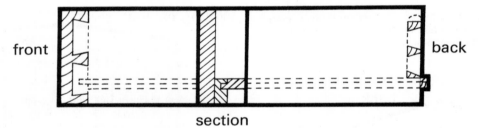

front   back

section

Sideview of traditional drawer

back

side

Traditional drawer construction showing solid bottom held by drawer slip and slotted screw.

drawer slip

direction of grain

24

PLYWOOD BOTTOMS

Plywood is now more often used for the bottom of a drawer than solid timber because of its stability and convenient thicknesses, which allow simpler methods of fixing to be used.

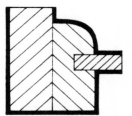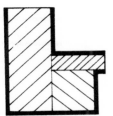

Sections through drawer sides

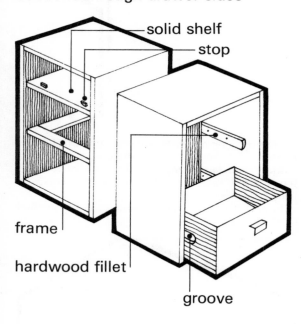

solid shelf

stop

frame

hardwood fillet

groove

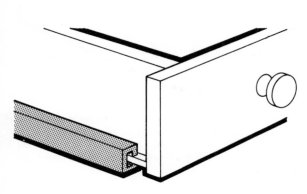

DRAWER FITTING

Small drawers inside a cabinet are guided by the sides. They bear or run on a shelf and have the underside of the next shelf or top for a kicker. This is a piece of wood which prevents the drawer from tilting downwards when it is opened and spilling its contents.

Stops can either be placed near the front or back to position the drawer and to prevent it from striking the back.

In larger cabinets, such as desks, runners and kickers may consist of frames screwed to the sides, thus saving weight and expense.

Softwood drawers with thicker sides may have the sides smoothly grooved with a machine router and may be suspended from hardwood fillets. These occasionally need waxing with tallow. They act as drawer stops and runners, and eliminate the need for kickers. Another method uses a section of Swish Furniglyde screwed to the side of the cabinet and the drawer base as a runner.

As the weight of the drawer is taken on the base, simple butt joints may be used in the construction of the rest of the drawer.

When making the drawer, allowance must be made for the track on each side. Plywood, 4 mm thick, is recommended for the drawer base and as the base is a runner it must extend on each side by 4 mm to engage in the track.

APPEARANCE OF DRAWERS

Traditionally the drawer front fits exactly the space made to receive it and is flush with the carcase edge. The solid front may be treated to make the front view more interesting, e.g. by chamfering the front surface to create a 'fielded' panel.

Alternatively, the front may be extended to cover the horizontal cabinet rails, thus giving a clean appearance. The top edge will provide a finger grip, if an alternative to the applied handle is desired. Traditional or simplified drawer construction may be used.

Absolute simplicity of line is achieved by using applied drawer fronts to the basic drawer. The fronts come from sheets of plywood 9 – 12 mm thick, if they are to be painted, or from veneered chipboard, if they are to be polished. Drawer stops are not required and handles are kept simple, often being recessed.

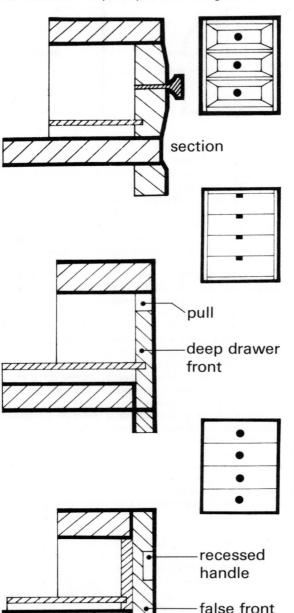

section

pull

deep drawer front

recessed handle

false front

EXAMINATION QUESTIONS

CORNER JOINTS

1. Show by means of sketches, satisfactory ways of joining, other than by nailing, screwing or dowelling, the two pieces of wood shown in figs A and B. (AEB)

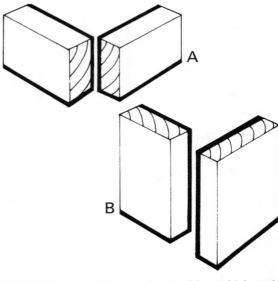

A

B

2. The drawing below is of a small box which could be made in either softwood or hardwood.

Make and name freehand drawings of *four* different ways that the sides of the box could be joined together.

In each case give the advantages of the method used. (MET)

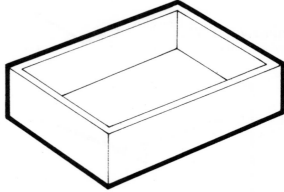

3. Name the two parts of a dovetail joint and state the angle or slope used when marking them out.
4. What would you expect to happen in a dovetail joint if the slope of the dovetail was (a) too great, (b) too small? (S)

5. Sketch a dovetail joint that could be used at the corner of a tray.

6. Make two sketches showing the difference between a through dovetail and a lapped dovetail. (JMB)

SIDE JOINTS

1. Pieces of wood have to be joined together as shown in the drawings. Use sketches to show two suitable joints in each case and indicate the circumstances in which each of these four joints should be used. (AEB)

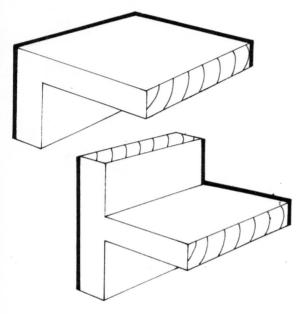

2. The sketch below shows the lower part of one end of a book rack using through mortise and tenon joints. The tenons have been wedged. Is anything wrong? If you think there is, what is it? (SE)

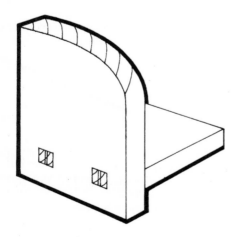

3. Draw the joint used for fixing a division into a cabinet.

EDGE JOINTS

1. Name the joint used to join the boards shown in the drawing below.

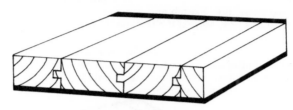

2. A table top has to be made up from three hardwood boards.

(a) Name and sketch two methods of joining the boards edge to edge.

(b) Illustrate how you would arrange the boards to minimise warping. (NW)

3. Which of the joints below is the strongest? Give reasons for your choice.

4. You have to make a circular table top 500 mm in diameter from two pieces of mahogany each 550 × 300 × 19 mm.

(a) Name three suitable joints.

(b) With the aid of sketches describe in detail one method of joining which you have suggested.

5. The drawings below show two accepted ways of joining boards edge to edge. Give one example where each method would best be used and give reasons for your choice.

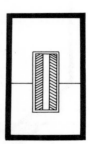

CONSTRUCTING THE BOX OR CARCASE

1. A strong box is required to hold nuts and bolts. It needs to be about 200 mm long, 150 mm wide and 100 mm deep, with a sliding plywood lid. The box will be heavy when in use, therefore the bottom of the box must be secure. Sketch and describe how you would make this box, stating the thickness of the wood and the joints you would use. (S)

2. A mineral specimen display tray is to be made from timber 50 mm wide and 12 mm thick. The inside has a number of compartments.

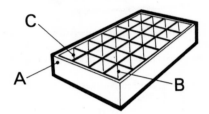

With the aid of free-hand drawings, show the details of how:
(a) The corners of the tray are jointed at A.
(b) The partitions are jointed at B.
(c) The partition is secured to the inside of the tray as at C.
(d) The base is fitted so that it is concealed from view at the sides.
(e) Name a suitable material for making the partitions.
(f) Name a suitable finish for the whole display tray. (MET)

3. The cabinet shown below stands on a plinth 75 mm deep. Explain how you would make this plinth and make a sketch of the joints you would use at the corners. (S)

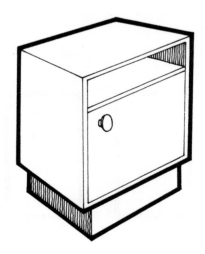

4. The drawing below shows an open-fronted bookcase with fixed shelves.
(a) Name and make a freehand drawing of the joint at A between the side and a shelf. Explain why you think this joint is the most suitable.
(b) Name the joint at B and explain why you have chosen this joint.
(c) Name a suitable joint for C.
(d) Name a suitable joint for D.
(e) Show with sketches how the plywood back is screwed in place so that the edging of the plywood is hidden. (MET)

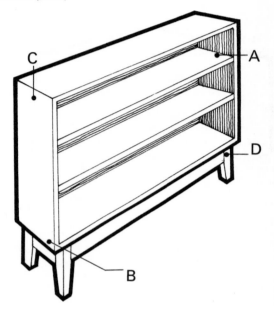

DRAWER CONSTRUCTION

1. Draw a rectangle 150 mm long × 60 mm deep. In it sketch the side elevation of a drawer, showing the joints used on the front and back corners.
Draw a similar rectangle, and in it sketch a cross-section taken through the centre of the drawer from front to back.
Sketch (approximately full size) a section through a drawer slip. (SE)

2. Show, by means of a freehand sketch, a method of fitting a drawer bottom to a drawer side, other than by ploughing a groove in the drawer side.

3. (a) Sketch and name **two** alternative ways of jointing the front of a flush drawer.
(b) Sketch **two** methods that can be used to provide runners for a drawer.
(c) What is the function of a kicker?

STOOL CONSTRUCTIONS

2

43 INTRODUCTION

The word 'stool' refers to a number of constructions which play a supporting role in furniture manufacture.

Stool constructions vary from low, fireside stools to table-top supports, and from bookcase underframes to dining chairs. The different names given to these constructions include 'leg and rail' and 'table'. Leg and rail joints have been a tradition in stool construction for many centuries, but other joints, borrowed from various types of box and frame constructions, are also used. For this reason similar joints may appear under more than one heading.

The three main constructions shown opposite are:
1. **Leg and rail**
2. **Deep frame**—which includes box joints
3. **Flat frame**—which includes frame joints

When choosing a construction for a stool, table or chair, take account of the fact that its appearance can be altered considerably by the type of construction used.

Look at the three illustrations of LOW TABLES. Even though they are all of the same size and similar shape, each has a different 'character' because of the stool construction used for support. Decide which of the three you prefer and which would be acceptable in your own home. (See page 30.)

When designing a low table it is best to make sketches of how you would like the finished job to appear and at the same time to consider which type of construction would be suitable.

Look at the illustrations of HIGH TABLES, LOW STOOLS and HIGH STOOLS and note how objects designed to meet the same functional requirements, differ in appearance, mainly because of their construction. (See pp. 30, 31.)

The drawings are not made to the same scale.

Leg and rail

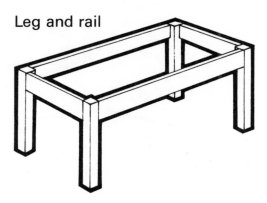

Deep frame

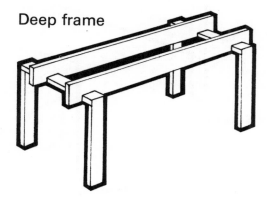

Flat frame

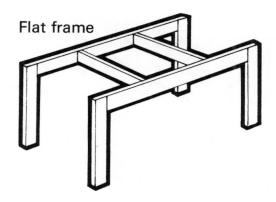

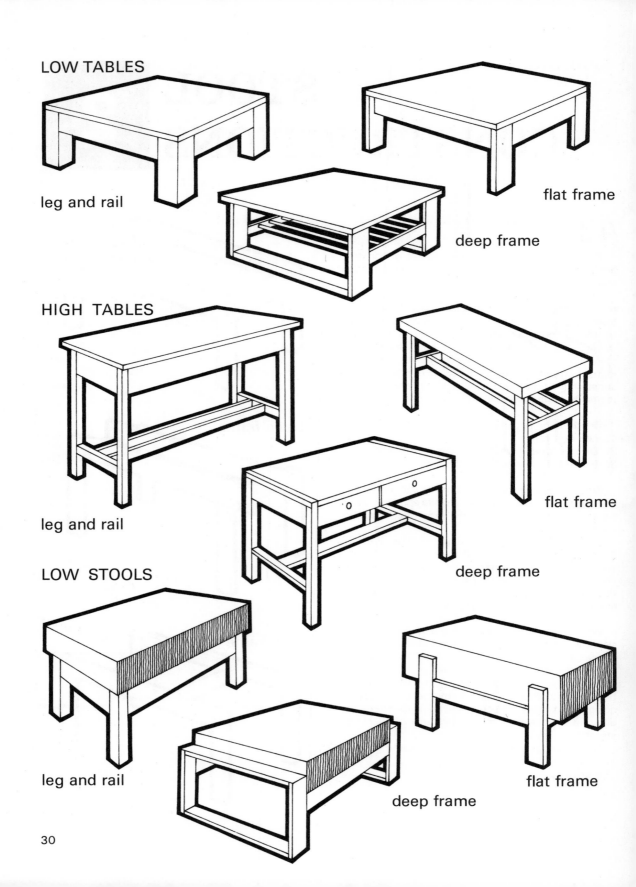

LOW TABLES

leg and rail

flat frame

deep frame

HIGH TABLES

leg and rail

flat frame

deep frame

LOW STOOLS

leg and rail

deep frame

flat frame

HIGH STOOLS

leg and rail

deep frame

flat frame

THE MORTISE AND TENON JOINT

The traditional stool consists of four legs, usually square in section, joined together by four rails.

The joint commonly used to join the rails is a mortise and tenon (A). In work where the tenon will not be seen, a square haunch is often used (B). Where the top of the joint will be visible, a sloping haunch is more suitable (C).

TENONS

(A) The simplest mortise and tenon joint lacks strength. Flush corner joints would be spoiled if the rail were to warp.

A

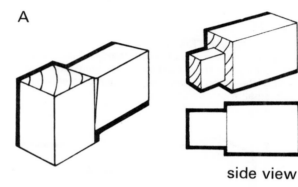

side view

(B) The square haunch is as long as it is thick and is one-third the depth of the tenon. If it is made larger, the mortise which is cut to receive it will weaken the leg.

B

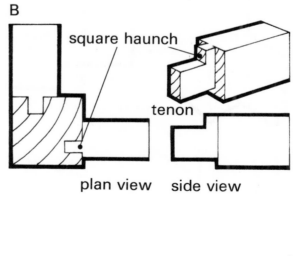

square haunch

tenon

plan view   side view

over ▶

(C) The sloping haunch has the benefit of strength and is also invisible when assembled.

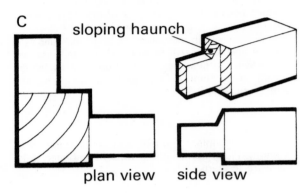

sloping haunch

C

plan view   side view

THE FORKED TENON

Occasionally a top rail more than 100 mm wide is used. Since a large mortise would weaken the leg, part of the tenon is removed to make two tenons and two small mortises are cut.

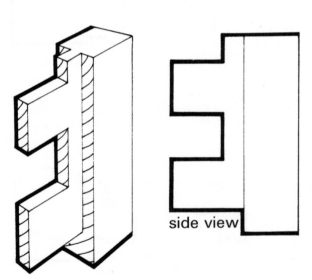

side view

THE MORTISE

The mortises made to receive the tenons are cut so that they meet inside the leg. This ensures that both tenons, if they are mitred at the ends, are of maximum length. The mortises are set towards the outside of the leg, not less than 6 mm from the edge, giving a large gluing surface and strength to the joint. Usually the tenon is one third the thickness of the rail—a fact that may affect the width of the shoulders.

Where the rails are 'flush', the tenon is set in the centre of the rail.

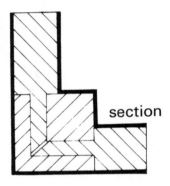

section

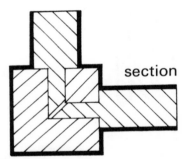

section

Where the rail is 'set-in', the tenons are short and comparatively weak.

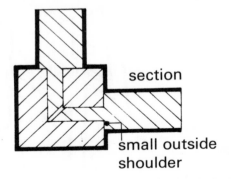

section

small outside shoulder

This fault can be overcome by using a smaller shoulder on the outside of the rail.

THE DOWELLED JOINT

Tests have proved that the dowelled corner joint can be made to withstand similar stresses to the traditional mortise and tenon joint. The perfect mortise and tenon joint is twenty per cent stronger than a dowelled joint of similar size, but the perfect joint has to be cut by machine and not by hand! Thus, in many instances, the dowelled joint will be the stronger of the two.

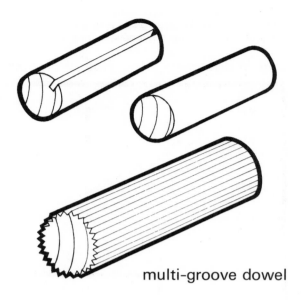

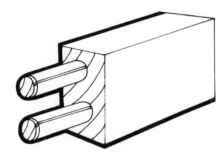

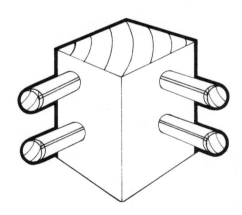

multi-groove dowel

ASSEMBLY

The length of the dowel must be less than the total depth of the two holes drilled to receive it. When the ends of each dowel have been chamfered (see *Woodwork 1, p. 120*), the whole surface of the dowel is glued and driven into the shallowest hole, which is usually in the leg.

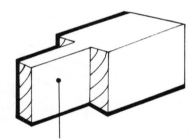

main gluing surface—if badly sawn, the joint is weak

THE DOWEL

The dowel must be of straight-grained hardwood and perfectly round in section. Beech is commonly used for dowel joints.

If a longitudinal groove is not machined into the dowel, then this is cut with a backsaw, or a dowel plate is used. (See *Section 40.*) Dowel diameters vary slightly but machined, multi-groove dowels are supplied, slightly oversize, and therefore always make a tight-fitting joint. The diameter of the dowel depends upon the size and type of job, but the 9 mm dowel is the one most commonly used.

The number of dowels used depends upon the width of the rail. A rough guide is to use two dowels for a 50 mm rail and three dowels for a 75 mm rail.

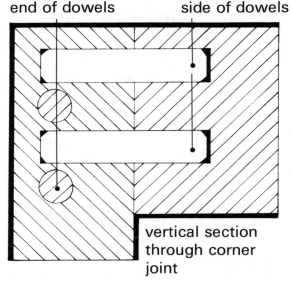

end of dowels   side of dowels

vertical section through corner joint

Note that the dowels are spaced so that each dowel may be of the maximum length.

THE DROPPED RAIL

The dropped rail is often employed to give extra strength to both the mortise and tenon and the dowelled joint.

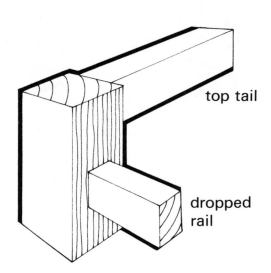

top tail

dropped rail

Dropping one top rail enables the tenons and dowels to be of maximum length and strength. In practice, the front rail of a chair is often dropped and the upholstered seat fitted into it (A). On low tables that are not too long, either the side or the end rail may be dropped (B). A long table must have the top supported along its length and so the end rails are dropped (C).

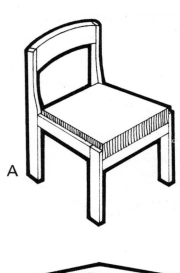

A

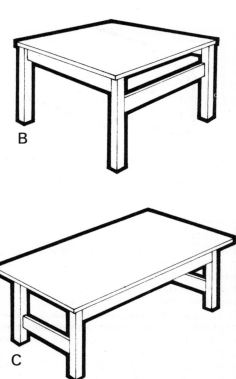

B

C

46 LOWER RAIL CONSTRUCTIONS

Lower rails are used below top rails to increase the strength of the construction, but they divide up space and alter the appearance of a piece of furniture.

Top rails can usually be made strong enough to join the legs together and also support the top.

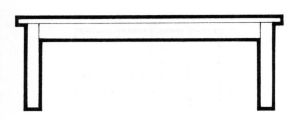

However, when narrow top rails are used, a lower rail gives the necessary strength by increasing the effective rail width. Lower rails can be used on any of the four sides.

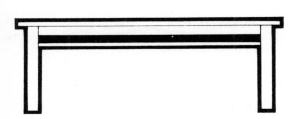

Taller tables, which support a writing surface or a cabinet, can be strengthened by using lower, narrow rails to 'tie' the legs together.

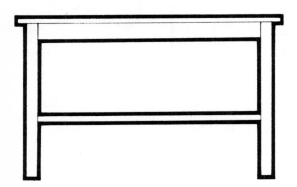

Lower rails can be arranged in a variety of ways as can be seen from the diagrams. If the article of furniture is designed for sitting at, then the rails must be set back or curved as in diagrams D and E.

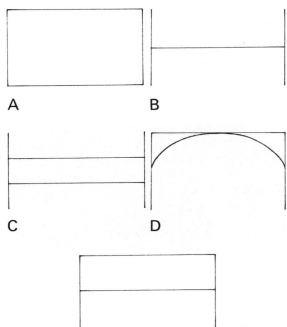

A

B

C

D

E

MULTIPLE RAILS

A multiple rail system (slats) is another way of introducing a lower rail construction. The rails are spaced so as to be decorative and they also act as a magazine and tray rack.

These lower rails can be used on all three basic stool constructions.

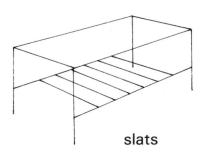

slats

SKID RAILS

Skid rails are lower rails placed at floor level, where they will give maximum support.

The skid rail is a traditional construction that has become popular in mass-produced furniture because machines can make all the joints of an end frame on one setting. This reduces manufacturing costs.

The skid rail is unsuitable if the piece of furniture is to be used on an uneven floor surface.

47 LOWER RAIL JOINTS

The shoulders of lower rail joints are best cut square and any taper of the leg taken from below the joint.

Dowelled joints can be used but mortise and tenon joints are more common.

Table with skid rail

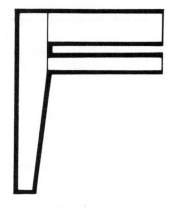

THE PLAIN TENON

This is generally used on softwood jobs and is the basis of more refined joints.

Stool with skid rail

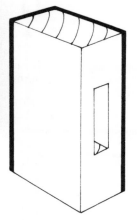
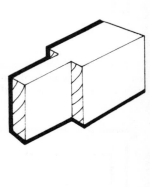

THE SHOULDERED TENON

Small shoulders at both top and bottom of the tenon give increased resistance to leverage and cover any accidental bruising at the ends of the mortise.

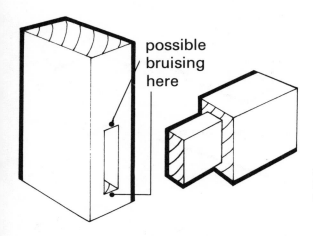

possible bruising here

THE STOPPED AND THROUGH TENON

In this joint the tenon can be stopped as in (A)—the stub tenon—or brought through as in (B)—the through tenon.

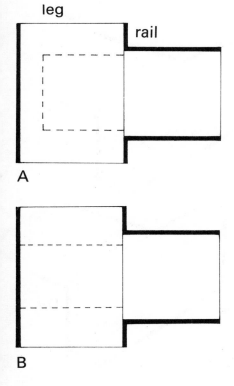

leg

rail

A

B

THE WEDGED TENON

A tenon is stronger if wedged from the outside of the leg as in (C).

C

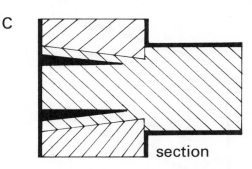

section

Wedges may be prepared from the same material as the leg or they may be fashioned from contrasting timber. They can be accurately sawn from a piece of 'waste' wood.

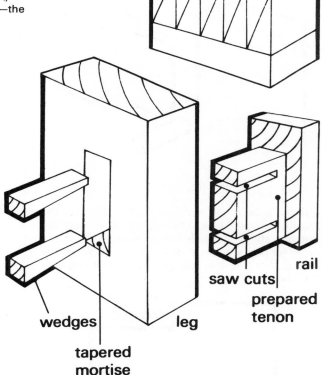

wedges

tapered mortise

leg

saw cuts

rail

prepared tenon

over ▶

Wedged tenons are most effectively used in a deep frame construction, where the rail enters through the narrowest part of the leg and has a limited gluing surface.

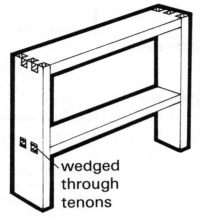

wedged through tenons

THE PEGGED TENON

A permanent fixing for stopped tenons can be obtained by gluing and inserting a length of dowel rod.

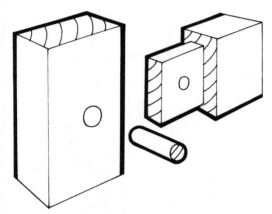

If the hole in the tenon is slightly closer to the shoulder than the hole in the leg, the dowel pulls the joint up tight. This is called 'draw-boring' and is most useful for long work, e.g. for dining tables, where the cramps available may not be of sufficient length to hold the joints together.

joint prepared for peg

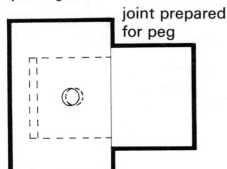

STRETCHER RAIL JOINTS

The rails which join underframes together—stretcher rails — can be fixed with a through housing (A) or a stopped housing (B) or the through tenon (C) or the stopped tenon (D).

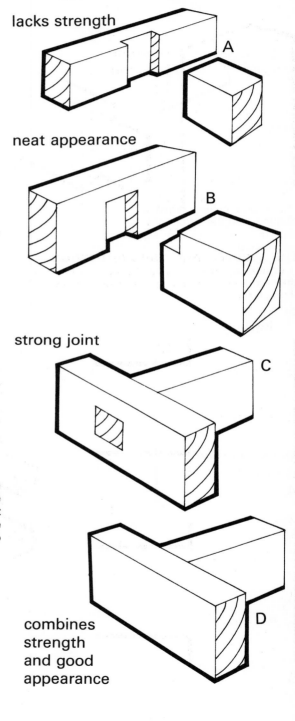

lacks strength

A

neat appearance

B

strong joint

C

combines strength and good appearance

D

Another method, which is simple, is to notch the rail onto the frame and screw it from below (E). (See also *Woodwork 1, p. 164.*)

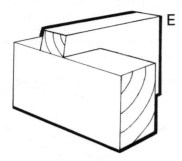

An alternative method is to use two pieces of Swish Furniglyde track running within each other. This is particularly suitable for use with manufactured board constructions. The hard PVC track is efficient and will not wear out as quickly as wood.

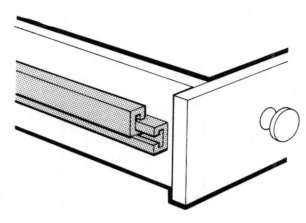

DRAWERS IN TABLES

Drawers are generally made as suggested on p. 24. Table and cutlery drawers, however, are usually shallow and the latter could almost be called trays. For these drawers the deep front or side rail is eliminated and replaced by two flat rails. A variety of joints can be used, but a simple and effective method is illustrated below.

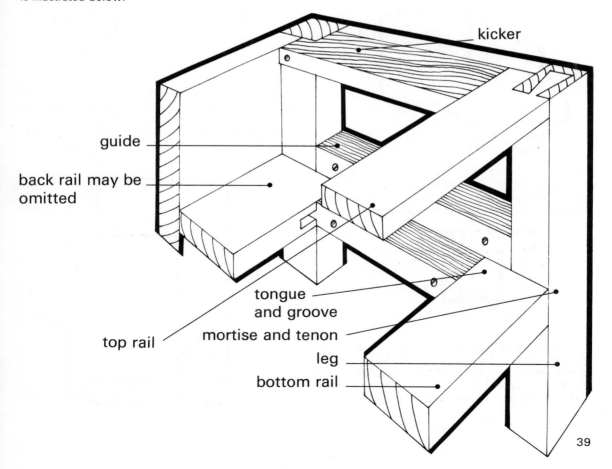

kicker

guide

back rail may be omitted

tongue and groove

mortise and tenon

top rail

leg

bottom rail

SUSPENDED DRAWERS

Lighter drawers may be suspended from the table top.

A fillet is glued and pinned to the top outside edge of the drawer side and a rebated hardwood runner is screwed into the table top from which the drawer is hung. If the drawer front extends beyond the sides, it covers the runners and acts as a drawer stop. This method is suited to a table without top rails on one side.

section

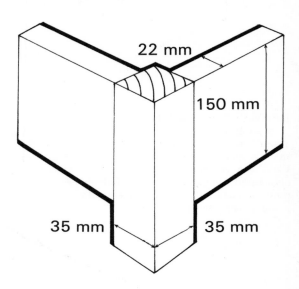

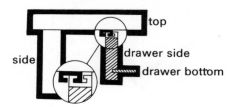

The drawing below shows Swish Furniglyde track fastened to the top edge of a drawer side (16 mm thick). The drawer is suspended from a similar track screwed to the underside of the table top.

Note: A length of Furniglyde can be screwed to the table top above the centre of the drawer and a barbed 'slider' fitted to the centre of the drawer back to run in the track.

Fit an end stop to the track to act as a drawer stop.

EXAMINATION QUESTIONS

TOP RAIL JOINTS

1. The incomplete sketch below is of the top corner of a table.
Draw, full size, an elevation of the joint you should use at the end of the rail, bearing in mind the width of the rail.
What size mortise chisel should you use? (S)

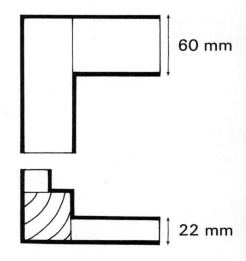

2. Make a full-size side elevation and plan of a rail (60 × 22 mm) jointed to a table leg 30 mm square by means of a haunched mortise and tenon joint.
Complete the views showing the hidden detail of the joint. (W)

3. Sketch and name three variations of the mortise and tenon joint showing how the common joint is adapted to meet different needs.

4. What advantage is there in wedging a through mortise and tenon joint?

Describe the process of preparing such a joint in hardwood for wedging. Mention:

(a) the modification to the mortise.

(b) the preparation of the tenon.

(c) the marking out and cutting of the wedges.

Make a sectional sketch of the assembled joint. (JMB)

LOWER RAIL JOINTS

1. The sketch shows a small table with one drawer, on which a television might stand.

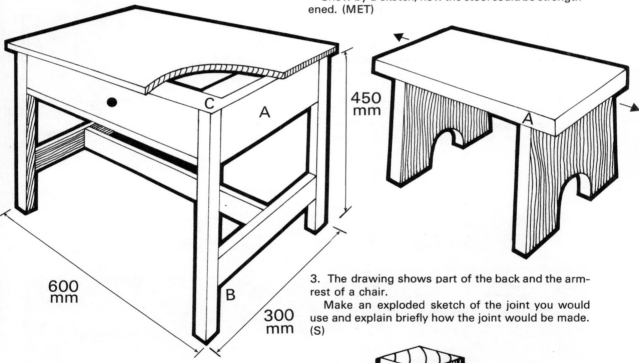

These details of construction are required:

(a) A sketch of the joint on the REAR end of side rail A which is 100 mm wide and 19 mm thick. (Do not draw any part of the leg.)

(b) A sketch of the joint at one end of stretcher B which is 30 mm wide and 12 mm thick. (Do not draw any part of the leg.)

(c) A sketch PLAN of the corner C where part of the top is cut away.

(d) A section of the edge of the top showing moulding which would improve the appearance.

Make all these sketches approximately full size. (SE)

DRAWERS IN TABLES

1. Make clear sketches to show the traditional construction of a good quality table with a drawer. Name the main parts and add notes to explain their function. The construction of the drawer need not be shown, but its position in relation to the parts of the table should be indicated.

Sketch a method of fitting a drawer stop and say why you think it to be sound. (JMB)

STOOL CONSTRUCTIONS

1. If you were making a pair of household steps, which joint would you use to fasten the steps or treads to the sides of the steps? (S)

2. The drawing shows a stool made in wood which, if used, would move as shown by the arrows.

Name and sketch a suitable joint for A.

Show by a sketch, how the stool could be strengthened. (MET)

3. The drawing shows part of the back and the armrest of a chair.

Make an exploded sketch of the joint you would use and explain briefly how the joint would be made. (S)

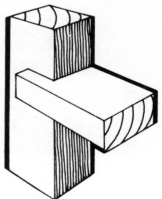

3 FRAME CONSTRUCTIONS

48 INTRODUCTION

The use of frames is common throughout all aspects of woodworking, their main purpose being to support panels of lighter timber or other material which might otherwise be structurally unsound.

In the sixteenth century, when the better carpenters became joiners, large chests made of heavy slabs of hand-sawn oak, nailed and strapped together, began to be replaced by frame constructions. Earlier examples of framed chests do exist, but they are rare.

Oak frameworks joined with pegged mortise and tenon joints were grooved to take thinner panels. These panels were often carved with a linen-fold pattern or they were pierced, which made them lighter still.

Slab construction

Frame construction with panels

(Crown Copyright, Victoria and Albert Museum)

Gradually the skill of joiners increased. Better tools became available and cabinet-makers began to fashion delicate furniture which did not always have the strength to withstand heavy usage. Nowadays, in this age of mass production, we have come full circle and the slab construction of a veneered chipboard linen box is very similar to that of its equivalent five hundred years ago. The nails and iron bands of medieval furniture have simply been replaced by the modern knockdown fittings.

In modern furniture-making, the frame often forms the basis of sideboard and wardrobe constructions and plywood panelled doors are hung on these frames.

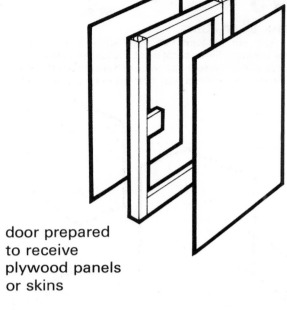

door prepared
to receive
plywood panels
or skins

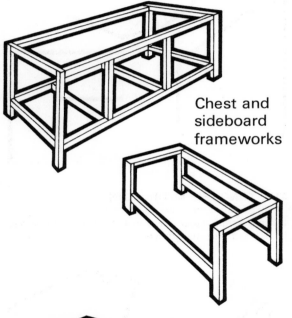

Chest and
sideboard
frameworks

Internal house doors sometimes have softwood frames covered with plywood skins, thus enabling them to be light yet stable.

Frames are also used for pictures and photographs in order to give them protection and improve their appearance.

In previous pages we have seen how frames are used in the making of stools and tables. They can, therefore, be adapted and used for many different purposes.

PARTS OF A FRAME

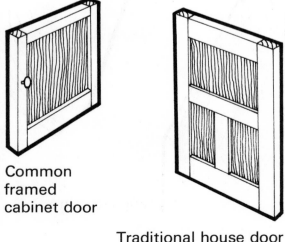

Common
framed
cabinet door

Traditional house door

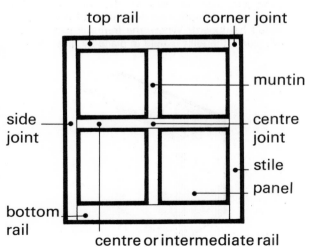

top rail

corner joint

muntin

side joint

centre joint

stile

panel

bottom rail

centre or intermediate rail

THE BUTT JOINT

This simple joint has little strength on its own for joining a frame but it can be made more secure by nails driven through the stiles or by corrugated fasteners driven into top and bottom rails and the stiles.

THE MITRE JOINT

When both the stile and rails of the frame are of the same width, the joint is cut at an angle of 45°. No end-grain is visible and the joint may be pinned and glued in place, using a mitre cramp. (See *Woodwork 1, p. 123.*)

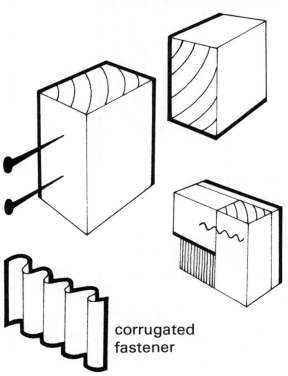

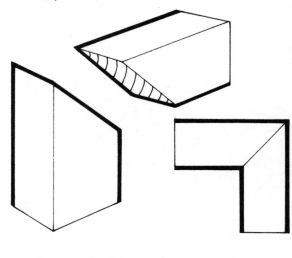

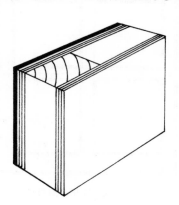

corrugated
fastener

THE TONGUED MITRE JOINT

This is an alternative to the mitre joint. The joint is run over a circular saw and a plywood loose tongue is inserted into the grooves.

The joint can be used for the framework of a simple door strengthened by a panel of plywood or treated hardboard. Where the frame is panelled on both sides, the joint is held in place by glue only.

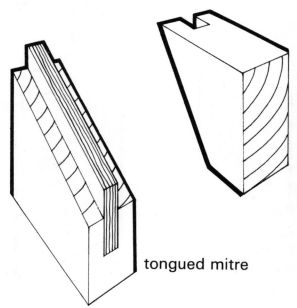

tongued mitre

REBATES AND MOULDING

Rebates, cut in the thickness of the frame, or mouldings, routered across the width, 'run round' the corners and make the material ideal for picture framing.

'Keying' with veneers, which are inserted into angled saw cuts, helps to strengthen the joint.

CORNER HALVING

This joint is used for simple frames, e.g. in the construction of garden huts and stage scenery. Its side-grain gluing surfaces and its shoulders make it stronger than the butt joint and it can be further strengthened by inserting screws, nails, or a dowel rod.

Half the thickness of the timber is removed at the corner from each stile and rail.

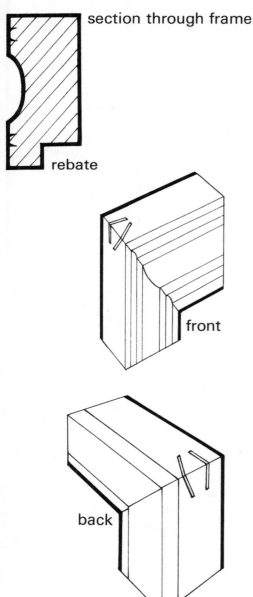

section through frame

rebate

front

back

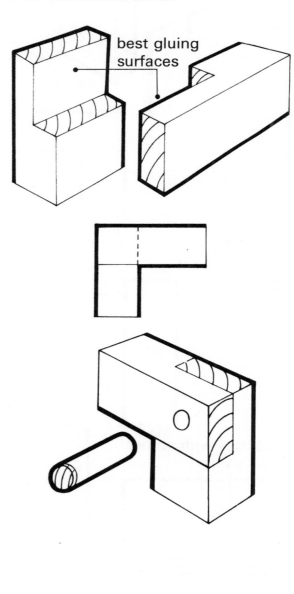

best gluing surfaces

THE CORNER BRIDLE

This joint is often referred to as an 'open' mortise and tenon. The open mortise is simple to mark out and more quickly cut than the closed one. If carefully made, it is attractive in appearance. The large gluing surface gives it considerable strength and the joint is often used on flat-framed stool constructions, e.g. for the supporting stool of a bookcase.

THE DOVETAIL BRIDLE

This joint needs care in marking out and in cutting but it is worth using when a corner joint is needed which will resist considerable downward pressure, e.g. for the suspended shelf of a wall-mounted vanity unit.

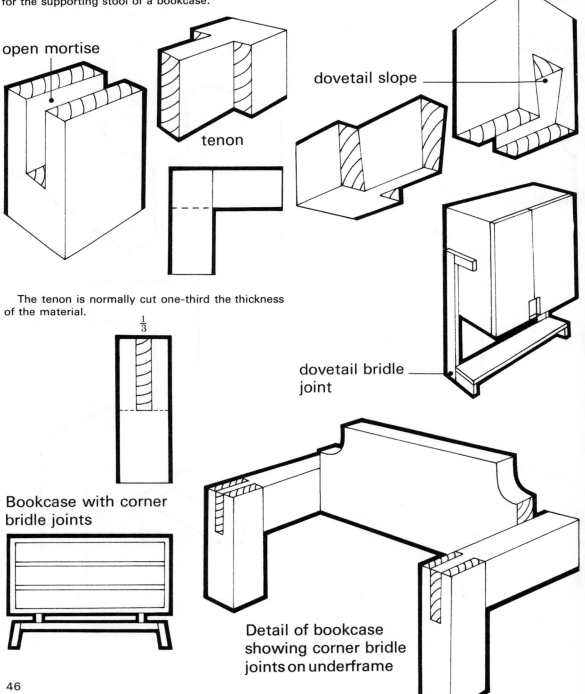

open mortise

tenon

The tenon is normally cut one-third the thickness of the material.

$\frac{1}{3}$

dovetail slope

dovetail bridle joint

Bookcase with corner bridle joints

Detail of bookcase showing corner bridle joints on underframe

THE MORTISE AND TENON

The shouldered, stopped mortise and tenon joint and the dowelled joint are both stronger than the bridle joint and are neater in appearance for frame construction.

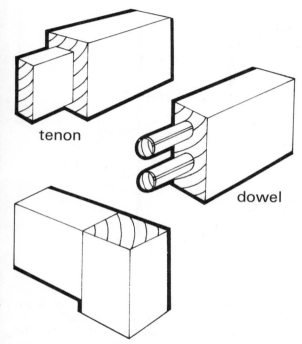

tenon

dowel

As in the leg and rail construction (see *p.* 31), the mortise and tenon joint is strengthened by using a square or sloping haunch.

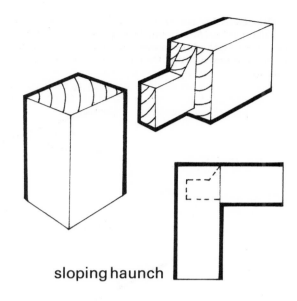

sloping haunch

Modifications of this joint include bringing the tenon through the stile and wedging it.

Some waste—called a horn—left at the end of the stile will prevent the short grain above the mortise from breaking out. The waste is removed after the joint is assembled.

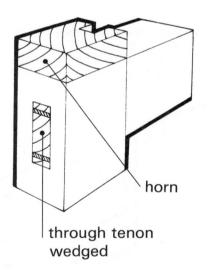

horn

through tenon
wedged

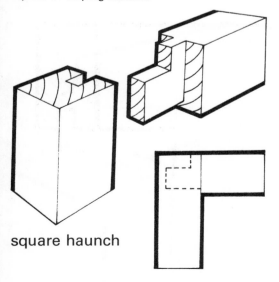

square haunch

over ▶

A guide to the proportion of the tenon can be seen in the rail illustrated, which is a common size for a rail. The length of the tenon depends upon the width of the stile and whether the joint is stopped or brought through.

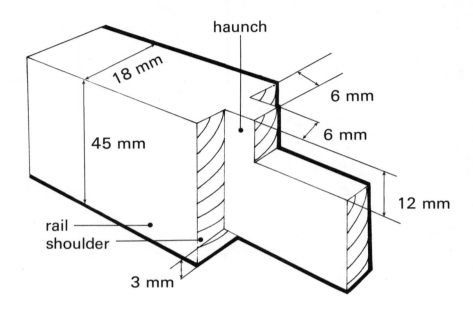

THE GROOVED AND SQUARE-HAUNCH MORTISE AND TENON

Carcases and door frames frequently support veneered plywood panelling inside a groove.

When the plywood is 6 mm thick, the tenon and mortise are cut to the width of the groove.

The groove requires a square haunch to fill what would otherwise be a gap at the end of the stile. The groove reduces the size of the tenon by an amount equal to the depth of the groove and the marking out of the mortise must be altered accordingly.

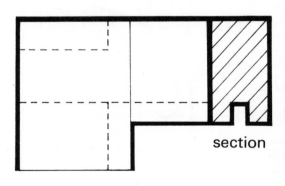

section

REBATED FRAMES

The traditional way of supporting panes of glass or mirrors is by using a rebate cut in the edge of the timber. In this way the pane or mirror can be fitted after the frame is assembled and they can be replaced if broken.

The rebate should be two-thirds the thickness of the wood and the joint is adapted in these ways:

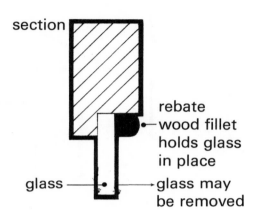

A haunch is not necessary on small doors. The back shoulder is longer than the front shoulder by an amount equal to depth of the rebate.

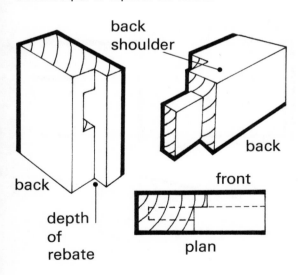

A sloping haunch can be used to give more strength to the corner joint and prevent the top rail from warping. It is suitable for doors in good quality display cabinet work.

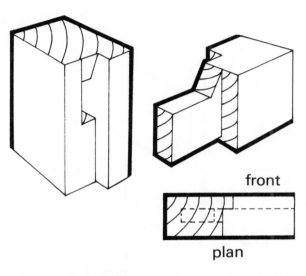

The square haunch joint is stronger and is suitable for large house doors and window frames.

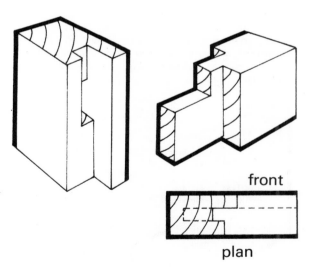

49

51 SIDE JOINTS

THE BUTT JOINT

The butt joint is used mainly in rough work. Dovetailed nailing through the stiles is common and corner blocks may be glued in to give added strength.

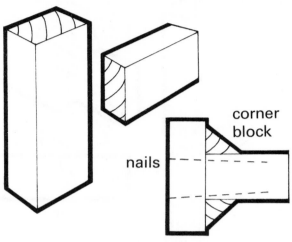

corner block

nails

Thin plywood gussets, glued and nailed, also strengthen the joint. These gussets are often found in stage scenery and are now also being used on the framework of upholstered chairs. With gussets, quite small-sectioned timber—down to 25 mm square—can be quickly and easily assembled and this method is replacing the heavy timber using traditional joints.

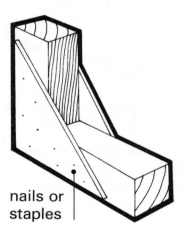

nails or staples

THE 'T' HALVING

The 'T' halving is commonly used for intermediate rails in stage scenery and for similar carpentry work.

The grain is cut across with a saw and the waste wood is removed with a chisel. (See *Woodwork 1, p. 49.*)

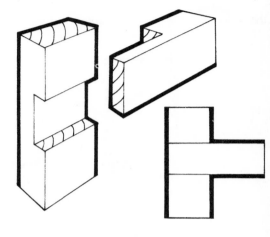

THE DOVETAIL HALVING

In a job where the 'T' halving would come under some strain, the dovetail halving is used in its place. The dovetail is cut first and the waste in the opposite piece of wood is marked from it.

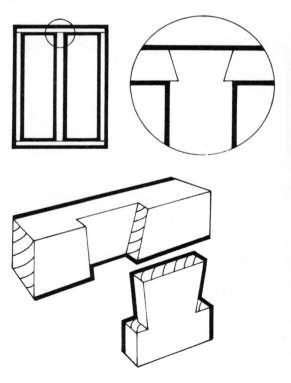

THE 'T' BRIDLE

This joint is marked out in the same way as the plain mortise and tenon but the 'opposite' pieces of 'waste' are removed. (See *Section 47—Lower Rail Joints.*)

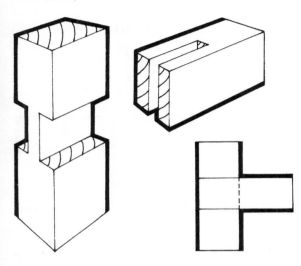

The 'T' bridle is a strong joint but in order to avoid gaps, the rail must be made to its finished width and cleaned up before the housings are marked out. In the example illustrated a good joint has been made, but rail edges A and B have been cleaned afterwards, leaving at best—a glue line, and at worst—an unsightly gap.

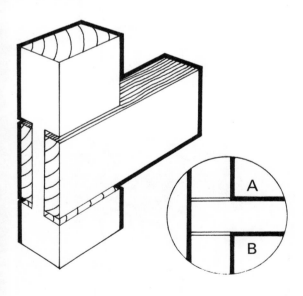

STOPPED SIDE JOINTS

In better quality framed work, stopped joints are employed, usually either the stopped shouldered tenon or the dowelled joint. (See *Sections 44—45.*)

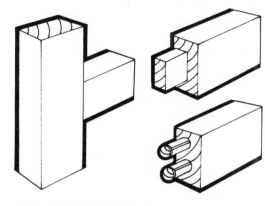

THE BAREFACED TENON

This tenon is cut with only one shoulder and is similar to a halving joint, the flush side being called 'barefaced'. It can be a stopped or through tenon and can be shouldered on the top and bottom edges.

The barefaced tenon is used in gate construction, where it may be desirable to fix match boarding flush with the surface of the framework.

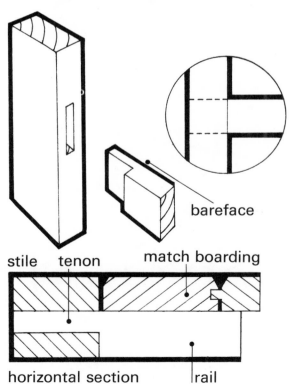

bareface

stile   tenon   match boarding

horizontal section   rail

52 CROSS JOINTS

THE CROSS-HALVING

This joint may be made in the width or the thickness of the rails.

In the illustrations below, joint A is used in flat frame constructions and joint B in deep frame constructions, for example, where the frames form the basis of an occasional table and where intermediate rails cross each other.

In order to avoid gaps, each piece must be cleaned up before the joint is made. The joint reduces the strength of each rail by half and, used on its own, it is not a strong joint.

In the common occasional table construction, lateral movement is often a problem. Four comparatively simple methods of reducing the effects of this built-in weakness are described below:

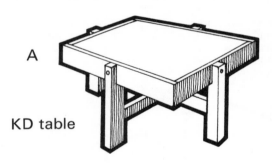

Weak table

Plan showing movement

In illustration A, the table top has been given a deep-frame lipping which acts as a top rail and is joined directly to the legs.

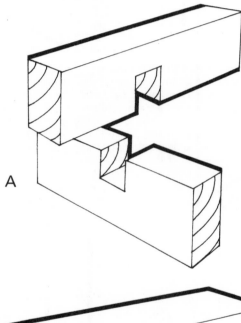

A

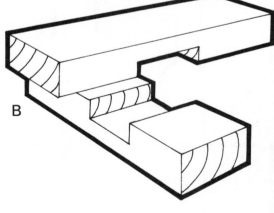

B

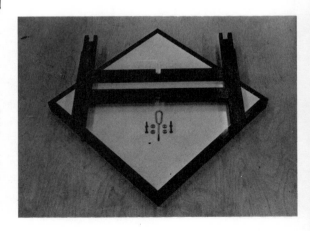

A

KD table

In B the rails of the frames have been made extremely wide and are therefore stronger.

B

Modern mass-produced table

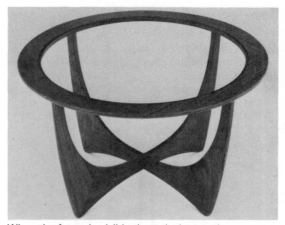

When the frame is visible through the top the appearance of the joint becomes important. The strong frames of this G-plan table are sculpted to make the joint as delicate as possible.

In C a lower shelf has been added to 'tie' the lower rails together.

C

Traditional hand-made table

In D the frame sections have been reversed thus giving a wider joint than in illustration B.

D

top
removed

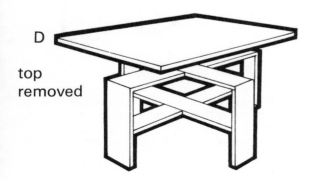

EXAMINATION QUESTIONS

FRAME CONSTRUCTIONS

1. Name two articles that you could make, using a framed construction. (S)
2. Name the type of joint commonly used in a framed construction. (S)
3. The sketch below represents a panelled door. Name the parts shown. (SE)

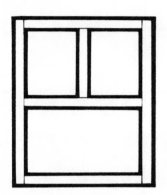

4. The sketch below shows the frame of a stool which is to have an upholstered seat.

Assuming that you are making the frame and that you have prepared your timber to size, explain by means of notes and sketches;
(a) The joints you would use.
(b) How you would set out the job.

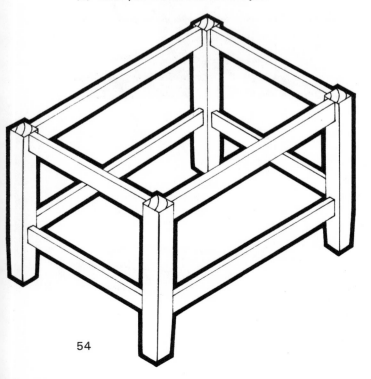

CORNER JOINTS

1. Make pictorial sketches to show two types of joint used at frame corners. Write a brief note to describe them and say where they would be best used.
2. The drawing shows a haunched tenon marked out and ready for cutting. The saw cuts are labelled A B C D E F.
Write down the saw cuts in the order that you would cut them when making the joint. (MET)

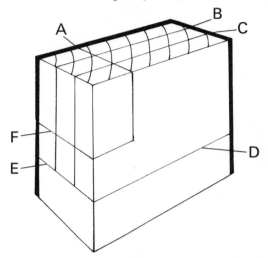

3. Name the three parts lettered A B and C on this joint and the hole into which this part of the joint fits. (S)

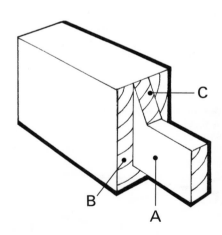

4. Comment on the design of the next joint suggesting any alterations which might improve it. Give reasons. Consider:
(a) The proportion of the tenon, its width and depth.
(b) The haunch.
(c) The shoulder below the tenon. (JMB)

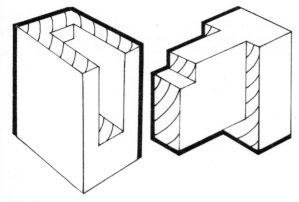

5. This incomplete sketch shows one corner of a mirror frame. The stile and rail measure 45 × 19 mm.

Draw full size the joint you should use at the end of the rail.

What size mortise chisel should you use? (S)

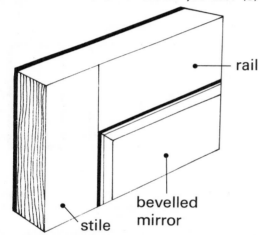

rail

bevelled mirror

stile

6. Draw the type of mortise and tenon joint you would use for jointing the pieces of wood shown below:

(a) Describe how you would mark out and cut both parts of this joint from timber which has been accurately planed to 50 × 19 mm.

(b) State, with reasons, at what stage you would cut the stile to its finished length. (AEB)

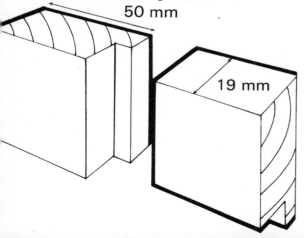

50 mm

19 mm

SIDE JOINTS AND CROSS JOINTS

1. Here are the elevations of two joints. What are their names? Draw an exploded view of each of them. By adding to your drawings show two different ways of strengthening the joints without using nails or screws. Both joints will be glued.

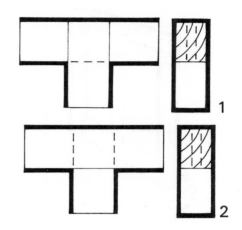

1

2

2. Make a free-hand sketch of a barefaced tenon. (S)
3. All these joints are used in frameworks. By what name are they known? (EM)

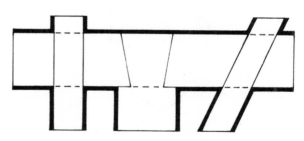

4. Draw these two pieces of wood, and on them show the marking out for a cross-halving joint. Show by shading, the wood that is to be removed. (WM)

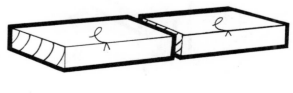

5. A glass-panelled firescreen is to be supported on two feet made from timber 200 × 75 × 19 mm. Make an isometric sketch showing the method you would use to join the foot to the bottom of the frame. The part of the frame to which the foot is jointed must also be sketched. Also design suitable shaping which will give maximum stability to the completed firescreen. (SE)

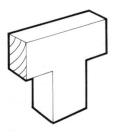

6. Make three copies of this drawing and show on them:
(a) A tee bridle joint
(b) A tee dovetail halving joint
(c) A through mortise and tenon joint

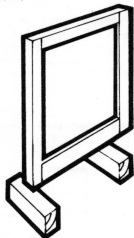

7. The drawing below is of a small child's work-table. The top has been removed to show the space which can be used for storing toys.

Name a suitable method of making each of the labelled joints. (SE)

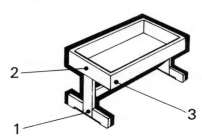

PANELS OF WOOD AND GLASS

1. Name the cuts A and B made on the edge of the rails illustrated below.

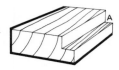 

2. Wooden panels in doors of framed construction are usually held in grooves. How are glass panels held in position? (S)

3. A B and C are sectional views of three stiles of separate doors. They need some further treatment.
A—to receive a glass panel
B—a solid wood panel
C—a mirror
Explain how you would prepare each of the three stiles, and draw sketches to show how the panels and mirror are fixed to the stiles. (W)

  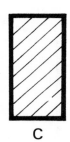

A   B   C

4. The construction of a cupboard door is shown below. The lipping and plywood are cut away to show the softwood frame.
(a) Draw sketches approximately full size to show a method of jointing (i) the corner of the frame; (ii) the corner of the lipping.
(b) Name the joints used.
(c) Briefly describe the method of fixing the plywood and the lipping to the frame.

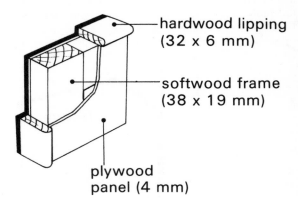

hardwood lipping (32 x 6 mm)

softwood frame (38 x 19 mm)

plywood panel (4 mm)

SLAB CONSTRUCTIONS

4

53 INTRODUCTION

The furniture-makers and designers of the eighteenth century were the first to use large quantities of fine Mahogany and Satinwood. These timbers were imported from the richly-forested countries of Africa and Central and South America. Mahogany and Walnut, which today are costly and used only for veneers, were then frequently employed in the making of furniture for upper and middle-class homes. Working-class homes continued to have furniture made of English timbers such as Oak and Elm for cupboards, and Beech and Yew for chairs.

Solid timber cabinets, however, often had backs of thin Pine and door frames were made to support lighter panels held in the grooves. Eventually, in order to satisfy the demands of the followers of fashion—the fashion of the wealthy—Mahogany furniture was made at a price which the less wealthy could afford. This was done by cutting veneers from the best boards and gluing them to a ground-work of cheaper timber. (See *Woodwork 1, p. 31*.)

PLYWOOD

In the nineteenth century, machines were developed which were capable of cutting thin veneers. These veneers were glued together, each piece being laid at right angles to the next to make plywood. Plywood then became a major material in the furniture industry.

Thin plywood, first employed for cabinet backs and door panels, was later applied to supporting frames— the basis of carcase construction—and a hard-wearing solid wood slab was used for the top.

Eventually plywood was made in thicker sheets— 'multiply'. These sheets were rigid, free-standing, free from movement and less liable to warp and twist than solid wood. Furniture could be constructed from plywood slabs only, without the support of frames. (See *Woodwork 1, p. 33*.)

Furniture made in this way and veneered with a fashionable timber, such as Teak, became very popular and is now within the price range of most people.

SOLID WOOD SLABS

A slab is a piece of flat, rigid material. This description fits very few specimens of solid wood since the wood must be free from the faults of warping, twisting and bowing—faults which can be eliminated in furniture construction by the use of battens or clamps.

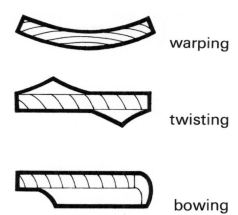

warping

twisting

bowing

BATTENS

Simple kitchen sideboards often have doors made from tongued and grooved boards, battened on the inside. Large drawing boards are made in a similar

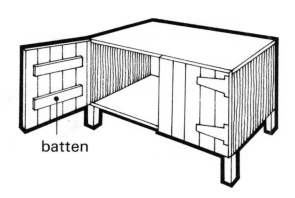

batten

way—the heavy-sectioned batten prevents the timber from warping and twisting. Shrinkage and expansion across the grain is allowed for by using slotted screws either side of a fixed centre screw. This avoids the possibility of the wood splitting.

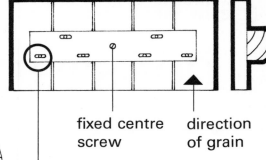

fixed centre screw direction of grain

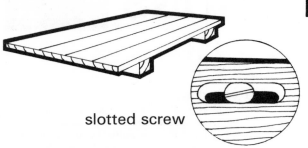

slotted screw

CLAMPS

Clamps are neater than battens since they are flush with the surface of the wood. They are frequently used on table tops. The clamps can be of contrasting timber as a form of decoration.

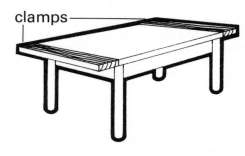

clamps

Three methods of clamping are shown opposite:
A is the tongued and grooved clamp.
B is the loose tongued and grooved clamp.
C is the tongued and tenoned clamp.

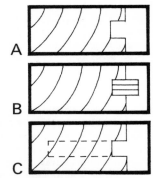

A

B

C

Wide surfaces which need clamping are often made up of a number of narrower boards, edge-jointed according to their size and thickness. (See *p. 20*.)

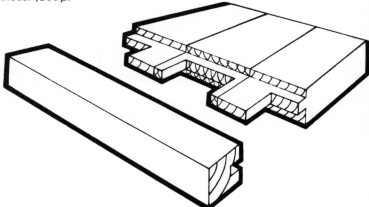

54 MANUFACTURED SLABS— EDGE TREATMENT

There are three main types of manufactured slab:

Plywood
Blockboard or Laminboard
Chipboard

For the composition of these slabs see *Woodwork 1, pp. 32—35.*

It is possible to buy these manufactured slabs, veneered on both sides and on all four edges, ready for finishing and use. Slabs cut from a large sheet, however, require treatment to hide and protect their edges.

PAINT

At present, painted furniture is in fashion and carefully finished plywood edges can be satisfactorily covered with paint.

Low stool with painted plywood ends.

VENEERS

Wood veneer can be applied to the edges of any type of slab. The veneer can be put on by traditional hand-laying methods but the use of pre-glued, iron-on edging strips or contact adhesives make the job easier.

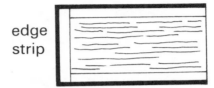

Wood veneer being applied to an edge.

PLASTICS

There are many types of soft, plastic strips, some resembling metal. You should, however, choose them carefully as a few can look cheap.

Both plastic strips and laminated plastic veneers, e.g. *Formica*, are fixed with contact adhesive.

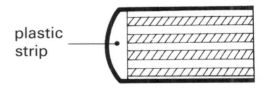

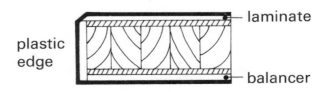

HARDWOOD LIPPING

Solid wood lippings wear better than matching veneers. They can be applied to a pre-veneered slab or to a plain piece before veneering. In the best work the corners are mitred.

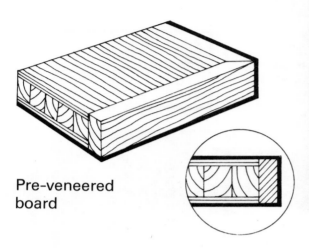

Pre-veneered board

Garden furniture.
Blockboard with a decorative
hardwood lipping

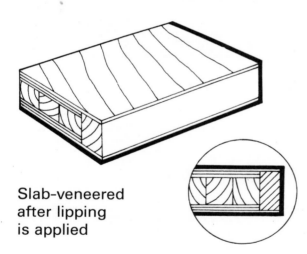

Slab-veneered after lipping is applied

SURFACE FINISHES

Slabs are used in a variety of constructions and the surface should be treated according to the purpose of the piece of furniture. Surfaces can be painted, or a polished veneer or plastic laminate can be applied.

Care must be taken to avoid bowing, when applying these surfaces to manufactured slabs. Use balanced panels with veneers of the same materials and thickness. The surfaces should be applied to each side of the core, but expensive surfaces, such as plastic laminate, can be balanced on the other side by a cheaper but similar material.

Note: If one surface veneer is finished thinner than another, bowing is likely to occur.

A wall unit with teak veneered chipboard panels dowelled into matching hardwood corner strips and fitted with a melamine surfaced hardboard back.

Three ways of applying the lipping are with:
- a butt joint
- a tongue and groove joint
- a loose tongue and groove joint

The butt joint is the simplest, but the loose tongue and groove is the strongest and is easily cut on a circular saw. When assembling these joints, edging cramps make the job easier.

55 FIXED CORNER JOINTS

Since manufactured slabs are unlikely to warp, the use of traditional corner joints, such as dovetails, is unnecessary. The joints shown below are for pre-veneered slabs and are not a ground-work for later veneering.

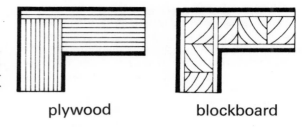

plywood   blockboard

THE BUTT JOINT

This simple joint, when glued with a resin or PVA adhesive, has considerable strength. When a back is applied, it is suitable for simple box constructions such as bookcases.

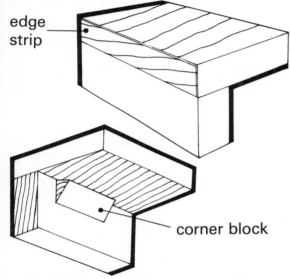

edge strip

corner block

Where the inside of the joint is not normally seen, a small corner block, glued in position with a contact adhesive, gives added strength.

THE REBATED OR LAPPED JOINT

This joint is effective in manufactured-slab constructions, but the 'end grain' is not easy to hide. In plywood or blockboard the 'end grain' is often stained but with chipboard, a veneer has to be applied.

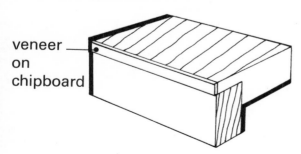

veneer on chipboard

THE MITRED JOINT

An accurately-cut mitre need only be glued but it is more often supported by a corner block.

Large widths may have blocks which are screwed and glued.

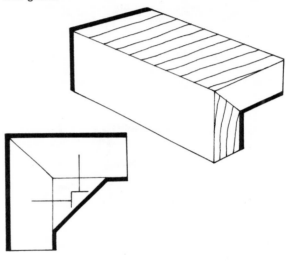

On larger, heavier work, using plywood or block-board, a loose tongue may be inserted in the mitre. It would normally be cut on a circular saw.

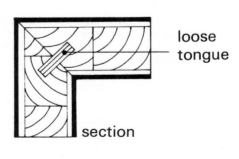

loose tongue

section

SPECIAL NAILS AND SCREWS

With the exception of blockboard and laminboard, the edges of manufactured slabs are not suitable for normal nailing and screwing. Plywood often splits when nailed and normal screws do not easily hold in chipboard, although long screws of large gauge number (say, 50 mm No 12) have good withdrawal strength.

GKN Twinfast screws, with double threads and Pozidriv heads, are stronger and easier to insert in manufactured boards than normal screws.

A *hardwood dowel* glued into the edge of chipboard will increase the holding power of a normal screw and the *nylon plug* shown is designed for use with Twinfast screws (gauge Nos 6 to 10).

Fischer nylon plug

Häfele 'Confirmat' screws are used in pairs on each corner of a chipboard box to make a stable construction. A carefully prepared pilot hole is needed but such is the unique thread design that a plug is unnecessary.

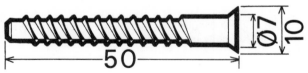

Manufactured slabs used on less important work, e.g. kitchen or outdoor constructions which are to be painted, can be nailed with **ring-shanked nails** designed for boat-building. Holes should be pre-bored in plywood.

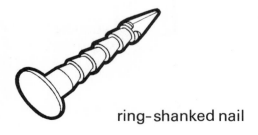

ring-shanked nail

THE CORNER LEG JOINT

The screwed corner blocks of a slab-sided cabinet can be developed into legs, if this is required. This often occurs in such items of furniture as a radiogram with plywood surfaces.

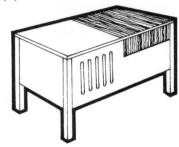

The slab can be flush with the corner leg as in illustration (A), or recessed as in (B).

The slab can also be tongued and the leg grooved, or both pieces grooved and a loose tongue inserted as in (C).

Another variation is the rebated slab, used when the leg is to be curved as in (D).

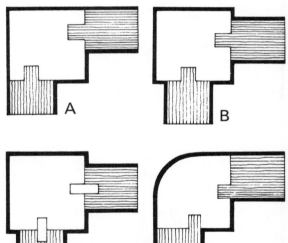

56 FIXED SIDE JOINTS

THE THROUGH AND STOPPED HOUSINGS

The cutting of both these joints in manufactured slabs is simpler than when using solid timber. (See *Section 39*.) Pre-veneered boards are accurately machined to size and only need rubbing down and polishing before joining together.

As no allowances need be made for cleaning up shelf-surfaces, the housings can be cut with confidence. If an electric router is used, the task will be much easier.

ADJUSTABLE SHELVES

Slabs in the form of adjustable shelves are best made from plywood or blockboard. The latter should have the core running along its length.

All the bearers shown in the illustrations can also be used with solid wood shelving.

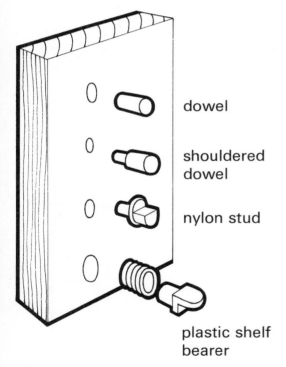

dowel

shouldered dowel

nylon stud

plastic shelf bearer

THE DOWEL

Shelves can be fitted on short lengths of dowel, which can also have a shoulder.

THE NYLON STUD

The nylon stud is an inexpensive substitute for dowelling.

THE PLASTIC SHELF BEARER

A hole is drilled to accommodate a bush into which the plastic shelf bearer is lightly hammered. The bushes allow shelf heights to be altered frequently without the holes being worn away.

THE TONK'S FITTING

For home use, shelves need comparatively little range of adjustment. If you make a cabinet which must have a full range of easily adjustable shelving, the Tonk's fitting is ideal. Strong metal bearers hook into metal strips which are recessed along each side.

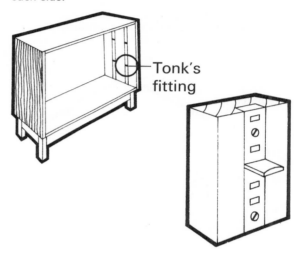

Tonk's fitting

SLAB CONSTRUCTIONS AND THEIR USES

Slabs, mainly of the manufactured type, are being increasingly used in a variety of situations, but are most noticeable in bedroom, nursery and outdoor furniture. The photograph below is an example of one of the simple designs that can be obtained with slab-constructed furniture.

57 FIXING SLAB TOPS

Slabs used for table tops often suffer damage through years of regular use and should therefore be easily removable for renovating. Both solid wood and manufactured slabs are now used for table tops.

BUTTONS FOR SOLID WOOD TOPS

Hardwood buttons are the traditional device for fixing solid wood tops. They allow the top to shrink or expand and at the same time prevent warping or twisting. They are slotted into individual shallow mortises, as in the illustration, or put in a groove cut the full length of the rail. They are mostly used on small, occasional tables where the ends of the top are not clamped.

METAL PLATES FOR SOLID WOOD TOPS

A set of metal plates, which do an effective job, can be quite easily made. Brass is the best material but steel plates, painted black and fixed to the top with a round-headed, japanned screw, are also satisfactory.

The plates are recessed into the top edge of the rail and slotted to allow for movement.

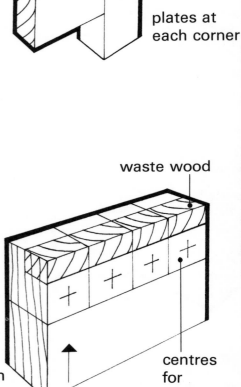

plate

plates at each corner

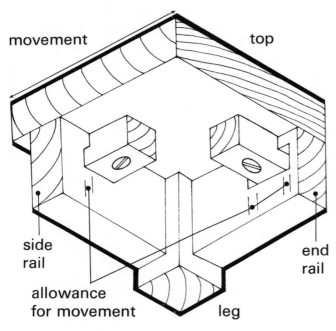

movement   top

side rail

allowance for movement

end rail

leg

Buttons are prepared on the squared end of a board; the sizes vary according to the size and thickness of the top to be held.

End of board on which buttons are prepared.

waste wood

grain direction

centres for boring screwholes

MANUFACTURED WOOD TOPS

Manufactured slabs do not 'move' and can be screwed directly into place.

It is possible for a top to be screwed through a flat, top rail but with a thick rail a carefully-cut pocket is often used. This is known as pocket-screwing. The pocket is generally marked out in pencil and chopped out with a chisel and gouge.

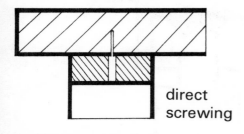

direct screwing

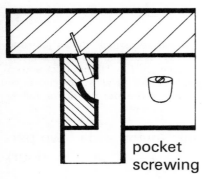

pocket screwing

An alternative to this method is counter-boring. A hole is bored into which the screw-head will fit. It is important to check the length of the screw and the use of the depth-gauge on a drill is invaluable.

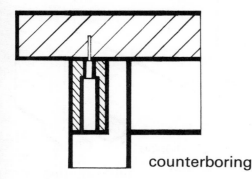

counterboring

Another effective method is to use plastic KD fittings. (See pp. 70–1.) Four are needed for a small table top.

58 SLIDING DOORS

Plywood, blockboard and chipboard are ideal for sliding doors, although the larger and thicker sizes tend to be rather heavy.

There are also many types of plastic/vinyl-covered, hardboard sheets available for vertical surfaces, e.g. *Laconite, Formica, Storeyboard H.* Their lightness, stability and attractive range of colours and patterns, make them ideal for panels in cabinet doors or sliding doors. The material can be worked in the same way as standard hardboard with hand and machine tools.

USING TRACKS

Thin sheet material and glass doors are usually run inside the grooved carcase, or set in a pair of tracks made of hardwood or plastic.

The depth of thc top groove is twice that of the bottom groove. The door height is indicated on the drawings below.

When using tracks, the bottom track may be fitted into a rebate in order to avoid an awkward lip on which the contents of a cupboard may catch.

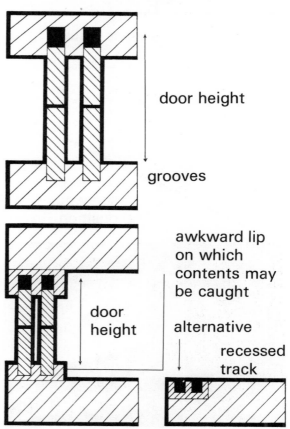

door height

grooves

awkward lip on which contents may be caught

door height

alternative

recessed track

INSERT AND SURFACE TRACKS

Small doors of thicker material can be grooved to run on nylon or fibre insert or surface tracks.

Insert tracks are grooved and glued into the carcase, top and bottom.

Surface tracks are secured with a contact adhesive and pinned.

Doors can also be fitted with nylon runners on the bottom edge to reduce friction.

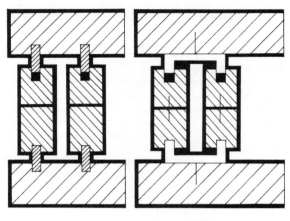

insert track   surface track

HUNG DOORS

Large kitchen-unit doors or wardrobe doors can be more easily slid back and forth if they are hung from a plastic or light alloy track.

The sketch of the *Glydor* track shows just one example of the many types available. This example is suitable for doors which are 12—19 mm thick and up to 9 kg in weight. In order to allow for clearance between pairs of doors and under the doors, follow the manufacturer's instructions.

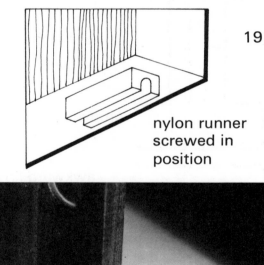

nylon runner screwed in position

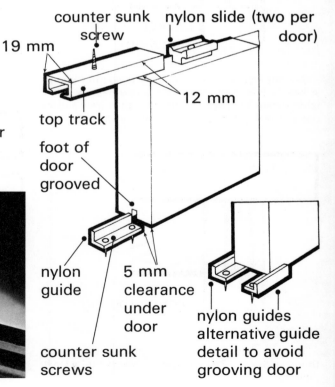

counter sunk screw

nylon slide (two per door)

19 mm

12 mm

top track

foot of door grooved

nylon guide

5 mm clearance under door

counter sunk screws

nylon guides alternative guide detail to avoid grooving door

ASSEMBLING CONSTRUCTIONS

59 GLUING UP

After many months of designing and making a piece of furniture or other woodwork construction, the time comes for it to be assembled or glued-up, and whether the work is large or small, careful preparation is necessary.

The equipment normally needed consists of:
1. A flat-topped bench
2. Clean cramps—set to length
3. A selection of cramping blocks
4. A pair of winding strips
5. Squaring rods
6. A soft-faced hammer

The normal procedure is for the job to be assembled 'dry', that is without using glue, and tested for accuracy so that adjustments can be made.

Do not attempt to glue up too much work at one time. Large jobs can often be glued up in several sections and end frames of tables or stools are connected to each other only when they are set.

GLUING UP EDGE JOINTS

It is common practice to make the boards wider than their finished size so that it is unnecessary for cramping blocks to be used. The bruised edges will be removed when the top is cut to the finished size.

T-bar sash cramps are employed (see *Woodwork 1, Section 23*) because they will not distort and they have a large slide area. An odd number of cramps, used alternately, will help to keep the boards flat. Test for flatness with a straight edge.

BOX CONSTRUCTIONS

It is most important that cramping blocks are carefully prepared for the assembly of box constructions, i.e. the blocks should be cut to a length equal to the depth of the box.

It does help if each block is planed slightly convex on its inside surface (the glue is squeezed from the centre of the joint first) but this is not essential with small work.

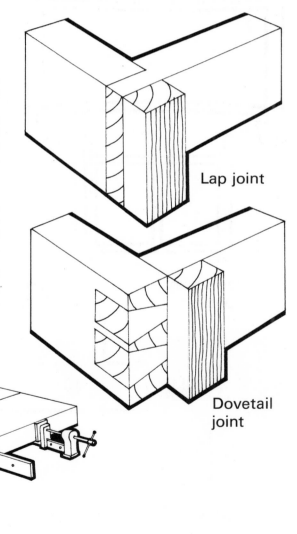

Lap joint

Dovetail joint

Where a lap joint is used, the blocks are placed in line with the end of the box, but where wood is not flush, e.g. in dovetail joints, the blocks must be set up to the shoulder line.

Do not overtighten the cramps, or position the cramping blocks away from the joint, as this will result in the sides bowing. Test with a straight edge and, if necessary, insert a temporary spacer. Test also with a squaring rod to see if the box is square and if it is not, adjust the cramps and re-check, (See *Woodwork 1, Section 15*.)

FRAME CONSTRUCTIONS

If stopped mortise and tenon, or dowelled joints are being used, it will be more accurate to cramp without using blocks. Where a through joint is used, however, blocks must be specially made to fit over the protruding tenon.

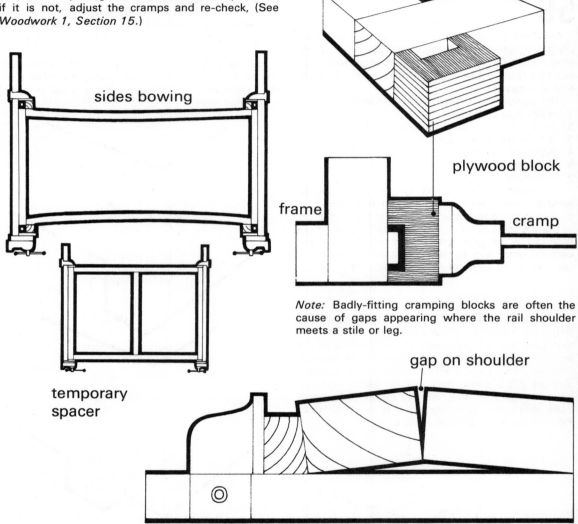

Note: Badly-fitting cramping blocks are often the cause of gaps appearing where the rail shoulder meets a stile or leg.

The use of T-bar cramps on a flat surface will help to glue the frame flat, but testing with winding strips is still necessary. (See *Woodwork 1, Section 15*.) If the frame is not square, the cramps must be adjusted accordingly.

GLUING UP DOWEL JOINTS

1. When gluing up dowel joints, PVA glues must be spread evenly over the whole surface of the smooth dowel to be effective.

2. UF glues are to some extent gap-filling and should be used with the multigroove dowel.

The strength of a dowel joint comes from the even film of glue around the dowel and the hole. Thus, a smooth dowel joint which is too tight suffers from 'glue starvation' and a badly-shaped dowel leaves a thick glueline around the dowel, which weakens the joint.

The strongest joints are made with multigroove dowels and UF glue and they are used on table and chair frame constructions.

Note: Apply the glue to both dowel and hole to ensure maximum coverage.

CLEANING UP

Good joints will squeeze out the unwanted glue. This is normally removed in its wet state with a brush and hot water and wiped dry with a clean cloth. Make sure that traces of glue are cleaned from the bench top.

Note: When the cramps are removed ensure that the bars are free from glue before putting them away.

60 KNOCK-DOWN (K D) FITTINGS

Many items of furniture in everyday use in your home are designed to be dismantled and reassembled later. Large or awkwardly shaped items are usually made in this way, e.g. tables and wardrobes.

The main advantages to the manufacturer and retailer of mass-produced furniture are in a reduction in transport and storage space and, therefore, in cost. The consumer benefits too. His furniture is delivered in parts and assembled *in situ* thus making damage to interior decorations less likely, particularly in a new house or flat which rarely has space to spare. Such furniture is invariably constructed from man-made, veneered boards, for which the traditional woodworking joints are not necessary and are often unsuitable. They are joined by a wide range of fittings. Some of these are complicated and require precision machining for them to be effective, but others can be more easily fitted, using only the basic workshop tools. These simple fittings fall into two groups:
1. Recessed fittings
2. Surface fittings

RECESSED FITTINGS
The Nylon Chipboard Fastener

This will effectively join the corners of cabinets, e.g. bookcases and it only requires carefully prepared holes for fitting.

Nylon inserts are glued into the end of one board and self-tapping screws are driven into them, cutting a thread on the inside. The screw head remains visible. Normal No 10 wood screws can also be used.

A more refined version has a thread tapped on the inside of the insert to take a machine screw. The head of the screw is also tapped to receive a cover cap which gives a neat and attractive finish. The caps are 15 mm in diameter, or 25 mm in diameter in a brass or chromium plated finish.

Occasional table which packs
flat for easy storage/transport.

The Frame Connector

This two-part fitting consists of an aluminium barrel-nut which fits within the thickness of a 19 mm rail. It acts as an anchor for the socket-head screw which is inserted through the end framework and tightened with an hexagonal key. It is used in table or stool constructions where the joint need not be hidden. (See photographs.)

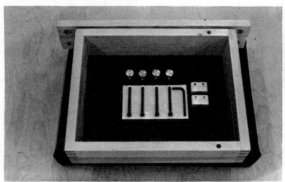

Stool frames (shown with seat removed) are joined to the rails with frame connectors.

Stool dismantled showing the frame connectors, hexagonal key and plastic fittings for fixing seat.

The Cross Dowel

The zinc-plated cross dowel is a neater alternative and is available in 14 mm, 20 mm and 25 mm lengths.

The Nylon Dowel

Nylon inserts are glued into each board. A connecting dowel joins the two components together with a firm, press-stud action making a strong invisible joint. They are generally used for carcase work for both corners and fixed shelves (See *Woodwork 1, p. 173*) but they have other uses.

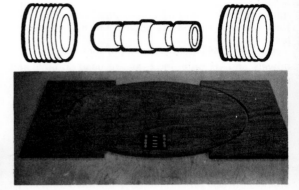

The oval occasional table is made from one sheet of veneered chipboard; the top is fastened to the base with nylon dowels.

SURFACE FITTINGS
The Plastic Fitting

This common fitting is recommended for securing underframes to table tops and cabinets but it can also be used as a corner joint.

Both plastic components are screwed to the parts to be joined. The dowels on one joint locate with sockets on the other joint and they are secured with a round-head machine-screw passed through one joint and into a metal nut in the other.

The plastic KD Block is more simple. It consists of one moulded component which is screwed between the angle of the pieces of wood. Both fittings are made in brown and white plastic.

The Joining Device

A fitting which does the same job as the plastic fitting but looks neater in appearance. It is fitted in the same way but a nickel-plated steel connecting plate, slid-on in the direction of the arrow, pulls the components tightly together.

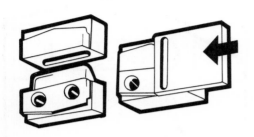

The Knockdown Dowel

A two-part brown plastic corner fitting which enables the construction to be dismantled frequently and quickly. A simple jig should be used to ensure accurate location of the dowels.

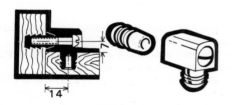

SUPPLIERS OF FITTINGS BY POST

Isaac Lord Ltd.,
185/7 Desborough Road,
High Wycombe,
Bucks. HP11 2QN

References

Nylon Chipboard Fastener	K650
Cover Heads	K1932 & K1125
Frame Connector: Barrel-nut	K200
Hexagonal Socket Screw	any length
Cross Dowel	K1250
Nylon Dowel	K632
Plastic Fitting	K6M
KD Dowel	K237 97100
Joining Device	K270

EXAMINATION QUESTIONS

BATTENS AND CLAMPS

1. A drawing board, table top or pastry board is clamped across the end grain.
(a) Why is this necessary?
(b) Explain how you would do this. (S)
2. Use sketches to show how your construction would make allowance for the movement of solid timber when:
(a) Screwing battens across the grain of a wide board.
(b) Fixing a table top to the underframe. (AEB)
3. Explain with the aid of sketches how you would make a good quality half-imperial drawing board of solid wood.
First suggest a suitable timber, giving reasons for your choice, and then explain the proposed method of construction. (JMB)

MANUFACTURED SLABS

1. Name a type of manufactured slab suitable for the following jobs.
In each case give reasons for your choice:
(a) Veneered shelves for a reference library unit.
(b) PVC covered desk top for a company director.
(c) A bedside unit resting on a plinth.
2. State one disadvantage of plywood as compared with solid timber when used in joinery or cabinet work, and explain how this disadvantage can be overcome.
3. Manufactured boards are used widely in woodworking today. Name two types you have used and show, by sketches, a way of using each in a school job. State why the material is more suitable for the job you have chosen than a piece of solid wood. (EM)
4. You are to secure hardwood lipping to the edges shown below. In each case state what method you would use. Give reasons for your choice.

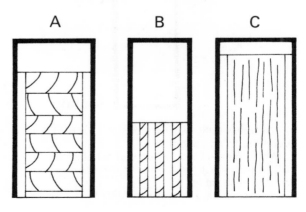

5. A manufactured slab is used for the following tops. Suggest a surface treatment for each one.

coffee table	art studio bench
kitchen unit	vanity unit
bedside cabinet	child's stool
dining table	bedroom chest
writing desk	garden table

SLAB CONSTRUCTION JOINTS

1. Make a full size drawing of a button suitable for attaching the top of a small occasional table. (JMB)

2. The drawing illustrates a design for a lounge table. The top has a plate glass inset which is not fixed in place, but can be taken out for easy cleaning.

(a) Sketch and describe in note form the construction of a suitable underframe.

(b) Sketch and describe the construction of the top, showing how the plate glass could be kept in place. In each case you must make clear sketches of all the joints you think suitable, and state whether manufactured or solid timber is used.

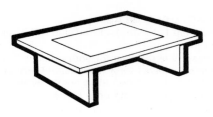

3. Make three copies of the section shown below and on each draw a different method of fixing a table or stool top to the rail.

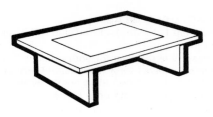

section

4. Describe fully two methods of attaching a solid wood top to an underframe.

Which method would be most suitable for:

(a) A small stool

(b) A writing table

Give reasons for your answer. (JMB)

5. The sketch is of a polished cabinet. Make sketches and notes to show how you would:

Join the side to the top at (A).

Join the fixed shelf to the cabinet side at (B).

Fix the plywood back (C) in position. (WM)

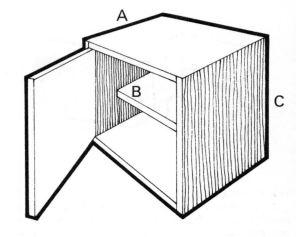

SLIDING DOORS

1. A wall cabinet 1000 × 225 mm is to have sliding doors. Describe fully:

(a) the materials and construction you would use for the doors and handles.

(b) the method you would use in the construction to enable the doors to slide.

(c) the method of fitting the doors to ensure smooth running.

(The use of plastic track is not allowed).

2. It is intended that the cupboard shown below will have sliding glass doors fitted. With the use of sketches and notes show how you would fit the glass doors. It must be possible to insert the doors after the carcase has been glued together.

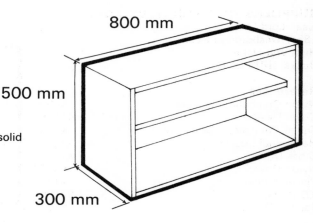

800 mm

500 mm

300 mm

GLUING UP AND ASSEMBLY

1. The drawing shows a cabinet door with a solid elm panel. Give an illustrated account of the checks you would carry out when gluing up the door.

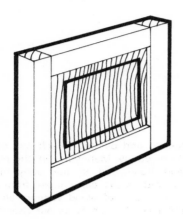

2. Show how it would be possible to place the sash cramps on the illustrated frame in order to pull the frame square. The error in the assembled frame has been exaggerated. Draw a straight line to indicate the position of each cramp.

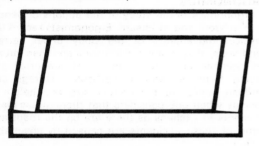

3. Describe fully the process of gluing up a drawer which has dovetailed joints.
   Name the type of glue used. (JMB)

4. *(a)* Use illustrations to describe the method you would use to glue up the frame shown below. The section of the timber is 50 mm × 25 mm.
(b) The following two faults could occur when gluing up the frame: 1. wind; 2. out of square. Describe fully how these faults could be corrected.

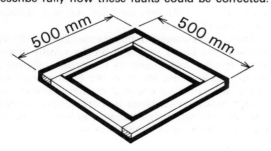

5. The drawing below shows one side frame of a kitchen stool. The legs and rails are joined by means of mortise and tenon joints which have already been cut.

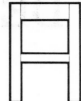

Describe how the frame would be assembled and the precautions that would be taken:
(a) to prevent the cramps from damaging the wood
(b) to ensure that the frame is square
(c) to ensure that the assembly is flat. (S)

6. Assume that you have reached the stage of completing the joints of a suspended bookcase (carcase construction). The top, bottom, and sides are joined with a common dovetail joint. Describe and illustrate how you would prepare the work for gluing and cramping. Give the following details in your answer:
(a) Method and purpose of 'dry-cramping'.
(b) Number and type of cramps to be used.
(c) Name of a suitable adhesive.
(d) The purpose of using cramping blocks.
(e) The position of the cramps on the work.
(f) The method of checking to see if the work is square.
(g) The method of correcting any error in squareness.
(h) The minimum length of time for work to remain cramped. (MET)

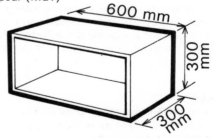

7. A strong box measuring 450 mm × 300 mm × 100 mm has through dovetail joints.
(a) Name the type of cramps most suitable for cramping the box together.
(b) *(i)* Give *two* reasons why cramping blocks should be used. *(ii)* Make dimensional drawings of *two* types of cramping blocks suitable for the above box.

8. Show how the use of plywood and new adhesives have affected design since 1939. Give examples of the various shapes and constructions which have resulted from the use of these materials, and the development of techniques associated with them. (W)

5 DESIGN

INTRODUCTION

This chapter looks at the problems of designing furniture against its historical background and notes the interesting ways in which our predecessors solved similar problems.

Each section sets out the basic needs of a design and then suggests at least one way in which those needs can be met. These suggestions are intended to begin a line of thought which will enable you to solve a particular design problem—your problem—in a personal way.

Four points should be borne in mind when designing a piece of furniture:
1. Materials
2. Finishes
3. Ergonomics
4. Modules

MATERIALS

The choice of wood will depend upon local resources and the money which you are willing to pay for each job. The constructions, based partly on your ability to make certain joints, are a factor affecting your choice between solid wood or manufactured slabs.

FINISHES

A look at the finishes given to cabinets on view at a recent International Furniture Exhibition in Cologne revealed the following results:

Walnut	25%
Painted or stained	25%
Veneer substitutes and laminates	20%
Oak	10%
Teak	7%
Rosewood	7%
Mahogany, Elm and other woods.	6%

Walnut tops the list in popularity and we have to go as far back as the sixteenth century before we find it as widely used as it is today. By the seventeenth century stained and painted Beech had come into fashion, followed by Mahogany in the eighteenth century and Rosewood in the early nineteenth century. Nowadays we can choose from all these finishes in the form of wood veneers and printed plastic laminates. We can make our choice of finish on aesthetic grounds and not be restricted by the cost or availability of a particular timber.

ERGONOMICS

Ergonomics is the study of the actions of people both at work and at leisure. Ergonomists record the physical movements of the body under certain conditions; they analyse the results and then inform the designers of our requirements. The importance of having furniture, and in particular, storage and working levels, of the correct size and height is obvious when one considers that there are as many accidents in kitchens as there are on the roads and some of these accidents are caused by unsuitable design.

MODULES

Furniture manufacturers are now designing fittings for modern houses which are built to standard units of measurement. These standard units are called modules. A very common module measurement is 100 mm.

If you are making large items of furniture such as storage units, it is more practicable to design your work on say 100 mm modules, so that standard fittings can be used.

There is a real need for this standardisation of basic items in the home. A check on the widths of such items in your own home as the cooker, the refrigerator, the washing machine, the bookcase or sideboard, will convince you that modular furniture and fittings make sense. Units that are not standardised probably vary so much in height, width and depth that they are awkward in appearance and in use.

DESIGN 1 UPRIGHT CHAIRS

Upright chairs have been referred to as 'activity chairs' because of the numerous jobs they are used for, such as eating, writing, sewing etc.

THE DESIGN PROBLEM

In the last five hundred years the upright chair has presented designers and makers of furniture with one of their most difficult problems—that of producing a standard size and shape of chair which is suitable for a great number of people of widely varying sizes and shapes.

By the seventeenth century chairs were strongly made and well-proportioned, but uncomfortable. Later manufacturers produced chairs with padded seats, which were more comfortable to sit on, but the intricately carved splats of the back, although beautiful to look at, were not so pleasant to lean against. The finely-made eighteenth-century chairs must have creaked considerably under the weight of prosperous gentlemen, who would have been more secure sitting on the simpler constructions of the country chair-makers of this period.

(Crown Copyright photographs, Victoria and Albert Museum)

It was not until the twentieth century that both strength and simplicity were combined in the upright chair, notably in the chairs designed in the Bauhaus in the 1920s. These designs were a direct result of studying the measurements of people and their need for support when sitting in an upright position. Since that time, the study of 'Ergonomics' and the introduction and use of new materials—steel and plastics—have enabled designers to meet our needs more closely.

1925 Chair with wicker seat and bentwood back support, designed and made in the Bauhaus

Carved chair c. 1690

Parlour chair—Thomas Sheraton c. 1790

Windsor chair c.1840

Both the chairs illustrated use modern materials suitable for mass production techniques. They are comfortable, efficient and are available in a variety of colours, yet many people dislike the materials of which they are made, and so the design problems of the modern upright chair still have to be solved in wood. Wood is more pleasant in appearance and also to the touch and is more in keeping with the furnishings of most of our homes.

Above: Hille chair in polypropylene.
Below: OMK 'Stack' in epoxy coated pressed steel.

THE SOLUTION

Giants and dwarfs excluded, research has shown that ninety per cent of the population need:

A firm seat platform 425—450 mm high.

A fairly low back rest, 725—850 mm high, which should slope slightly backwards.

A seat 450 mm wide and 400 mm in depth.

A design based on these measurements will give a satisfactory degree of support and therefore comfort for the limited period of time for which such chairs are used. Thin upholstery of the right type (see page 135) will soften the seat and back-rest, but thick cushioning will reduce the support that a well-proportioned chair can give.

THE CONSTRUCTION

Much of the success of a chair will depend upon how it is constructed. Its construction will determine its strength and appearance. The bad habit of users in tilting a chair back, places an enormous strain where the side rails join into the back legs.

The mortise and tenon or dowel joint used here can be strengthened with a wider and thicker rail or by adding a narrower, lower rail.

A heavier rail will allow twin mortise and tenons to be used or more dowels to be inserted—each increasing the gluing surface and therefore the strength.

Constructions using straight, square legs and rails, rather than round ones, are easier to make and are stronger.

A plywood base for the seat and back may be laminated on an open wood former and screwed to the framework. (See *Chapter 8, p. 129*). Arm-rests for upright chairs can be made by extending the front legs above the side rail. The arms are then joined to the front and back legs. Arm-rests should be 200 mm to 225 mm above the seat. When the arm joins the front legs, it does a strengthening job similar to that of a lower stretcher rail.

MATERIALS

Expanded PVC material is suitable as upholstery for upright chairs. It wipes clean and is hard-wearing.

Any available hardwood of the appropriate 'colour' can be used for the frame and Beech, either in its natural state, stained, or painted, is particularly recommended.

Note: If you are making a set of chairs, ensure that you have sufficient timber of the right kind to complete the job.

FINISHES

Hard-wearing lacquer and polyurethane finishes, which can be brightly coloured, are excellent for resisting scuff marks on the bottom of the legs.

DESIGN 2 HIGH TABLES

THE DESIGN PROBLEM

In many modern homes there is insufficient space for a dining room or a dining area. The dining table will often have to be used for other activities—perhaps as a desk or sewing table. Thus a table that can be made larger or smaller is an asset.

As early as 1600 this problem was solved by the invention of the draw table—the principle of leaves that can be extended from the ends of the table. In the seventeenth century, the gate-leg table was introduced—a circular table of which one half of the top folds over, so that it can be pushed against a wall to save space.

round gateleg table (seventeenth century)

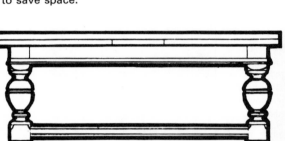

drawtable—about 1600

In previous centuries, dining tables had to be made with heavy legs in order to support the thick, solid table top. Today, when tops can be made of thinner slabs of material that will not warp, heavy legs are no longer necessary. Often legs are replaced by a light pedestal support in metal and plastic, but the traditional corner leg and rail construction in wood, although not imaginative, is more stable and reliable.

THE SOLUTION

Write down the minimum and maximum number of people who are likely to use your table at one time. Then, taking into account that people need about 600 mm of table edge at which to sit, and the shape of the space into which the table must go, you can decide on its size and shape. Where there is sufficient room for a round table this has its advantages. A 1200 mm diameter top will seat up to six people and with centre portions fitted, (making it a D-end table) eight or ten people could be accommodated.

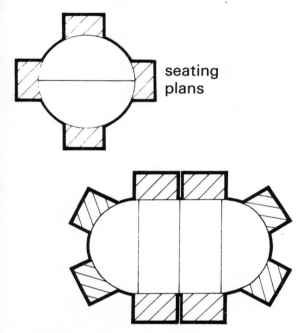

seating plans

The height of the table depends upon the seat height of the chairs and the thickness of the rails. There should be a space of 150 mm between the top of the seat and the bottom edge of the rail. Table top heights will vary between 700 mm and 775 mm.

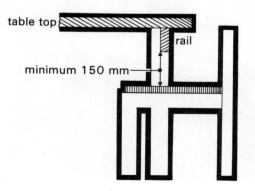

table top

rail

minimum 150 mm

THE CONSTRUCTION

Lighter legs and rails can be used when metal plates are employed to give support to the corner joints.

Manufactured slab tops can be fixed to the frame with metal plates. You can make these or use manufactured plates which have slots, designed to allow expansion and contraction of solid wood tops, which are useful to position accurately the top on the frame.

MATERIALS

For the underframe, use a hardwood to match the framework of the chairs. The top may be veneered with a plastic laminate of either a matching wood grain pattern or a plain colour—white always looks attractive.

FINISHES

The top must be heat-, scratch- and water-resistant to keep its good looks over a period of hard wear, and a matt, or eggshell finish is often preferred to a high gloss.

Plastic laminates using modern rotary gravure printing to produce a wood grain print can solve the table-top problem. A block Rosewood design is shown below.

DESIGN 3 EASY CHAIRS AND LOW TABLES

THE DESIGN PROBLEM

The function of an easy chair is to support a tired body—allowing it to relax. The old idea that the body can rest on large amounts of soft padding is a misleading one. You only need to watch television for an evening, sitting on very soft cushions, to notice how soon you become restless and fidgety.

Members of your own family may have their favourite 'arm chair' and it is reasonable to suppose that this is because it gives them adequate support and they feel comfortable—in other words, the easy chair is a 'good fit'.

The modern easy chair, with fully-upholstered covering, is a smaller descendant of the large Victorian leather-covered chair, which contained a mass of springs and hair padding.

Wood side frames, rubber webbing and foam for upholstery have made chairs much lighter, and castors for moving them have become unnecessary.

Easy chairs, using end-frame constructions, are still the best type for production in your workshop but, unless fashions change again, chairs made of wood may become a rarity.

Read this account of modern chair-making: 'Plastic chemicals are injected into a simple aluminium mould; they then set hard, producing a light, strong shell. After ten minutes the shell is ready for covering and for a variety of legs/bases to be attached'.

The polyurethane chair illustrated below was made by such a process and with almost no restrictions on the shapes possible, designers will be able to satisfy the individual needs of each person.

KD construction using thick plywood and securing the rails with Pirelli webbing—the seat platform.

THE SOLUTION

Design an individual chair based on the dimensions given below which extensive surveys have shown will accommodate most people.

Seat height at front:	350 to 400 mm
Depth of seat to back:	400 to 500 mm
Width of seat:	450 to 500 mm
Arm rests:	225 mm above depressed seat.
Height of backrest:	650 mm above depressed seat to give support to shoulders.

Note: The chair may be given an appropriate extension in height for a head rest.

The angle between the seat and the backrest on the chair below would be about 100°.

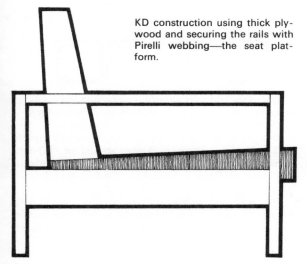

KD construction using thick plywood and securing the rails with Pirelli webbing—the seat platform.

CONSTRUCTION

Most chairs of this type consist of two side frames joined together by cross rails or bolted to the frames which support the upholstery. Seat webbing is used across the width of the chair keeping the cushions in place and allowing the front rail to be set low to give the seat a soft front edge.

MATERIALS

The frames should be of hardwood to withstand the hard wear they will receive. The seat foam should be hard, in order to give support, but the low backrest could be of softer material.

The upholstery covers are best made from a hard-wearing, woven material which is treated to resist stains from spilt drinks. They can also be fitted with a zip of *Velcro* so that they can be removed for easy cleaning.

FINISHES

The wood frame must have a hard, scratch-resistant finish.

LOW TABLES

Low tables are also referred to as occasional tables or coffee tables. (See *Woodwork 1, pp. 155—159.*) They are a comparatively recent furniture development and this fact has encouraged designs of all shapes and sizes in almost every material available.

The height of the table top should be directly related to your easy chairs. Placed next to or between chairs, it can be as low as 300 mm, although 400 mm is more common. For activities such as letter writing and card games, it is necessary to have a height of 500 mm to 600 mm.

DESIGN 4 DRESSING TABLE AND STOOL

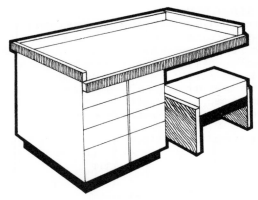

THE DESIGN PROBLEM

Throughout the centuries dressing tables have changed in style, but the basic requirements have remained the same. They are:

1. A mirror
2. Storage for cosmetics
3. Storage for small articles of clothing

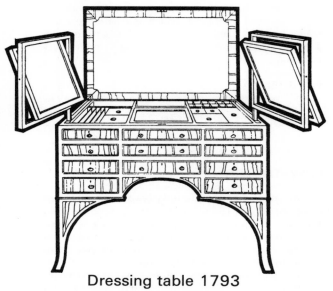

Dressing table 1793

Another effective solution consists of a full set of drawers in a cabinet to which is attached a table top. The idea is simple, makes good use of space and can be adapted for right- or left-handed people.

The manufactured board top is faced with a plastic laminate and has a projecting lipping on three edges— the front lipping being flush with the surface.

The top drawer is usually quite shallow (50 mm to 100 mm) and the bottom drawer should be 150 mm from the ground. The height of such a unit is about 700 mm and the upholstered stool should fit the kneehole space at a convenient height.

The size and position of mirrors is a dominant design feature. A wall-mounted, full-length mirror and an adjustable mirror on a stand, are the most serviceable combination.

The traditional dressing table has a kneehole so that it is easy to sit at, and the mirror is usually hinged, with two wings.

The dressing table of the future will probably be influenced by the fact that as more women go out to work, less time is spent sitting in front of a mirror. Additionally, the owners of small modern houses find that the space normally occupied by a dressing table has to be put to the best use and, in terms of space, the traditional three-mirror table is a luxury.

THE SOLUTION

Find out from the person who will use the dressing table what type of storage spaces will be required together with their approximate sizes. Consider whether or not a wall-mounted storage box with a mirror inside a hinged lid would not be more suitable.

CONSTRUCTION

The storage unit is a large slab construction fitted with drawers. (See *p. 86.*)

The fronts of these are attached to a simple box unit so that their decorative veneer is shown to good advantage.

Handles for the drawers are shaped from lengths of suitably contrasting timber—experiment with the appearance and feel of a variety of sections.

The slab-sided stool is screwed to a hardwood frame which supports a deep cushion on a plywood base.

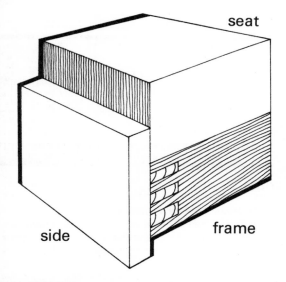

MATERIALS

Large flat surfaces of a good quality, veneered chipboard will not warp, are easily made up and can be given a variety of finishes.

Note: Choose an attractive board to make into drawer fronts.

The top surface and the shallow drawer bottom can be made resistant to chemicals, by facing them with a plastic laminate or a less expensive white polyurethane paint. A contrasting timber can be used for the hardwood lipping round the top and for the seat frame.

FINISHES

A wood finish must be resistant to marks from cosmetics, after-shave lotion etc.

THE DESK UNIT AND CHAIR

THE DESIGN PROBLEM

Designers in previous centuries have developed the writing desk from a simple box with a sloping lid to the stage when it became an ornate chest of drawers fitted with innumerable pigeon holes and secret drawers.

Left: Late seventeenth-century cabinet with mirrored doors enclosing drawers and pigeon holes and a drop-flap to form a writing surface.
Right: A small 'Lady's desk' designed by Thomas Sheraton in the late eighteenth-century. It has drapery behind the glass and a brass rim around the top.

Common sense has now prevailed and modern solutions are aimed at producing something more practical, i.e. a writing and typing surface, storage space in the form of drawers and cupboards. The modern desk is also smaller and therefore more suited to the small, modern house.

The design problem for the desk and chair is basically the same as that presented by the dressing-table and stool and can be solved in a similar way.

'Atlantic' Executive Desk veneered in American Walnut. Table using a slab construction with independent lockable storage units on castors.

DESIGN 5 BEDS AND BEDSIDE UNITS

THE DESIGN PROBLEM

Whilst most people in the Middle Ages slept in a communal bedroom, the master of the house had a chamber for his own use. His bed was large and rather hard, and the curtains which enclosed it at night were drawn back during the day and the bed was used as a couch. The eighteenth-century version shown had a French name—*Chaise longue* (long chair). It was too small for a comfortable night's sleep.

The dual-purpose bed is a feature of our times too and your design problem may be solved by using a bed which will 'double' as a daytime settee. Such a compromise has its disadvantages but the thinner and firmer mattresses available today make satisfactory seats. A modern way of solving the problem is shown below. The bed slides beneath a floor-standing unit and the pillows and other bedside clutter are stored behind the padded backrest.

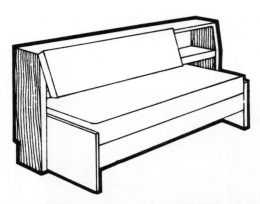

In 1660 one well-known gentleman had a bed for his bodyguard which, during the day, he kept beneath his own bed—a solution to the space problem that designers have recently re-discovered. His bed was 2150 mm long compared with our own standard mattress of 1900 mm. It seems that as people have grown taller with each generation their beds have become smaller!

Presuming that you want to make a 'normal' single bed, you have to choose:
1. A suitable mattress
2. A mattress base or platform
3. A base support

THE SOLUTION

1. A suitable mattress

Buy a standard size of mattress (1900 mm × 900 mm) with a degree of hardness or softness to suit your own needs. A spring interior mattress is unnecessary and a combination of a firm layer of polyether foam under a softer and thicker slab of latex is recommended.

The foam is glued to the base with a suitable adhesive, trimmed to size and covered with a cotton fabric which is stapled underneath. The mattress is then covered with a suitable material known in fabric shops as 'ticking'.

latex

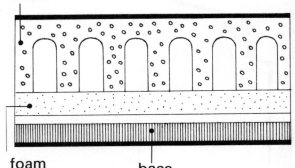

foam   base

2. Mattress Base or Platform

The base must be firm and flat—a sleeping surface which sags like a hammock will not give your body the support it needs. Choose from four alternatives:

(a) Softwood slats screwed to the frame.
(b) Six millimetre plywood slab with 12 mm ventilation holes at 75 mm centres.
(c) A perforated hardboard base.
(d) Standard *Pirelli* webbing interlaced across a strong frame.
Note: 9 widths and 5 lengths are required.

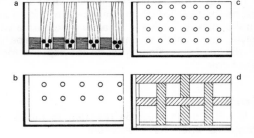

3. A Base Support

The base must be strong, stable and yet easily moved.

It should also clear the ground by 225 mm to facilitate cleaning beneath it or else it should rest on a box-like plinth.

Natural wood sides hold the mattress neatly in place and can be raised at both ends to create simple head and foot boards.

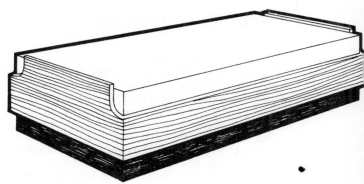

CONSTRUCTION
Mattress Base

Square-sectioned softwood with bridled corners can be strengthened by wooden slats, plywood or hardboard. A deeper framework will be needed if webbing is used and in addition to wood or metal corner brackets, two metal U-bars are normally necessary.

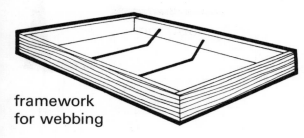

framework
for webbing

Base Supports

These vary according to the type of base used. The most simple consists of head and foot boards, bolted to a wide connecting bar with the hardboard mattress base screwed in position.

MATERIALS

Solid wood and plywood in substantial thicknesses are best suited to withstand the strains to which a bed is subjected.

Veneered chipboard is ideal for storage units.
Note: Use the webbing, foam and latex recommended by the manufacturers.

FINISHES

Surfaces can either be given a clear finish or painted.
Note: Black is recommended for plinths.

THE BEDSIDE UNIT—THE SOLUTION

The need for bedside storage will vary with the individual. Bedside cabinets are one solution but the modern preference is for smaller storage units attached to part of the headboard. (Continental Headboards)

Where skids are used in place of a plinth, the 'in-between' space can be used for storage.

Drawers are unsatisfactory as they collect dust but simple lidded boxes on mini-castors are ideal.

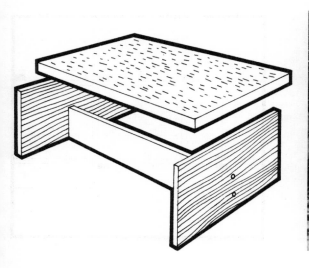

DESIGN 6 STORAGE UNITS

THE DESIGN PROBLEM

Because of the living and collecting habits of each individual there are as many storage problems as there are people. Storage units should be designed so that everything has a place and whenever an object is required, it can be readily found.

The areas into which a modern house is divided— bedrooms, kitchen, hall, dining-room, bathroom, living-room, garage, and garden, are activity areas which require different types and sizes of storage units.

Make sure that you are using your present available storage space to the best advantage. Items that are only required at certain times of the year, such as camping equipment and suitcases, can be put in less accessible storage places than things that are required every day.

When this sorting out process is complete, you are then in a position to make positive statements of your need for further storage units.

UNITS FOR A PURPOSE

Make a list of items and their sizes, which are to be stored together. You will then have an indication of the overall sizes of the unit required.

Where possible make the unit to a module which will enable further units to be added when a similar type of storage is needed.

Storage unit positions in a particular activity area must be considered 'ergonomically' and related to frequency of use. Research has revealed the recommended heights and positions of units in the kitchen activity area; these principles can also be applied to other areas—workshops and bedrooms in particular.

Interests and activities within a family differ and change with each individual, and units should be adaptable for purposes other than those for which they were originally made. The need then is for a basic unit into which different interiors can be fitted and which can be arranged in a variety of ways— principles on which many wall storage units are designed.

Such units can be based on a module system. They are really boxes fitted with either shelves, drawers, or doors which perform a variety of functions and which can be added to at a later date.

Note: People short of money have been known to use 'orange boxes' successfully to form storage units for almost every purpose!

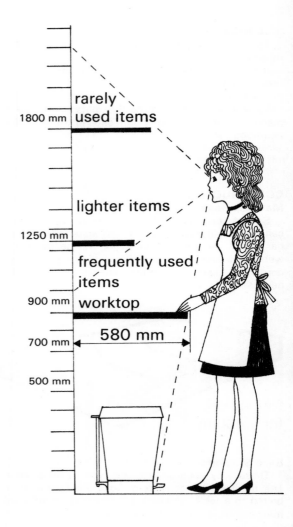

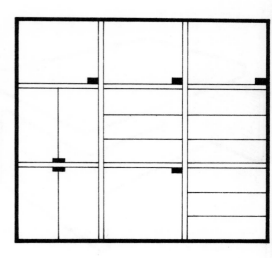

METHODS OF STORAGE

Consider whether the storage unit needs to be enclosed for any reason—security, cleanliness, appearance. If not, then it may be possible to use fixed or adjustable 'open' shelving.

Boxes fitted with shelves make excellent wall units and are easily enclosed with doors. Plan the fitting of doors carefully, remembering that they can open outwards, in the conventional way; they can be pushed up and pulled down, or they can slide in a track. Small storage drawers are better than large, heavy drawers, which are difficult to open and close and in which small items get lost. Locate the drawers below eye level so that their contents are easily seen. The use of enclosed cupboards, open shelving and drawer space is shown in the wall-mounted study/bedroom unit illustrated.

FREE-STANDING OR BUILT-IN?

Consider whether your storage unit is to be permanently fixed in one position in the house or whether it is to be free-standing. Built-in units are neat but their use is restricted.

Most of your units will be free-standing and the elimination of dust traps and ease of cleaning are factors to be considered in their design.

Note: Section 58 describes joints of slab constructions used in storage units.

The Hille Storage Wall System is flexible and compact. It includes washing facilities, clothes-hanging space, a desk top covered in PVC, with light above, and ample additional shelves for television, brief cases, hand luggage and books.

DESIGN 7 CHILDREN'S TOYS

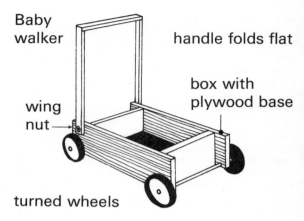

Baby walker

handle folds flat

box with plywood base

wing nut →

turned wheels

THE DESIGN PROBLEM

The three main problems are: the child's age
the material
safety

THE CHILD'S AGE

It is better to make a toy for a child whom you know and which he or she will understand and be interested in. Toys that are either too 'young' or too 'old' will quickly be rejected and remain unused.

THE MATERIAL

Design toys that are best made from wood rather than plastics. Such toys need to be strong and have some weight in them. Do not try to copy toys that are better made in plastics.

SAFETY

Particular attention should be paid in the planning stage to avoiding sharp edges, small pieces that may be swallowed, handles that protrude, and finishes that are easily chipped or may be poisonous.

THE SOLUTION

Assess the needs of the child—notice the toys which he plays with most happily and plan a toy that you think he will enjoy.

Simple toys can give a child an opportunity to use his imagination—an example of this is the multi-purpose brick.

Ensure that your design will be strong enough in normal use—and remember that 'normal' often means standing on it!

It would be a pity if the toy looked good but was easily destroyed.

SOME IDEAS FOR TOYS

The toys listed below are suitable for a wide range of children and are the basis upon which you can use your imagination to make 'new' ones.

Wooden rattles	Cut-out animals
Bricks	A rocker
A baby walker	A garage
An engine	Skipping rope handles
A mallet and pegs	A toboggan

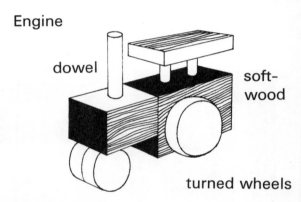

Engine

dowel

soft-wood

turned wheels

Hammer peg toy.

Model garage made from pine, hardboard and Perspex. The ventilated roof is detachable for easy access to the top floor and allows exhaust fumes to escape! The showroom has papered walls and a large window of clear Perspex.

Toboggan

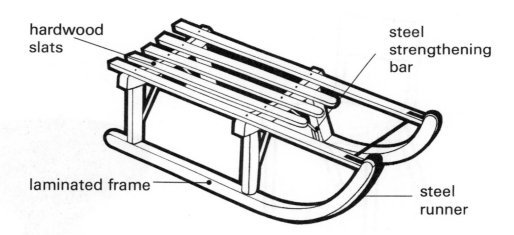

hardwood slats

steel strengthening bar

laminated frame

steel runner

CONSTRUCTION

Use modern adhesives which enable simple jointing methods to be employed. Avoid metal fittings but, where necessary, use screws instead of nails.

Toys, such as building bricks, which require many parts of the same size can be 'jigged up'.

FINISHES

Apply coloured finishes to wood where they will look attractive and contrast them with natural grain patterns which will interest children. Finishes which prevent the wood from becoming dirty, which seal the grain and which allow the toy to be cleaned easily, are adequate—one coat of cellulose or polyurethane is sufficient. Use only paint which is non-poisonous. Most manufacturers now make lead-free paints but it is safer to ask, before purchasing.

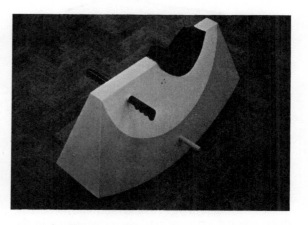

Rocker made from blockboard and plywood glued and screwed together. Finished in acrylic paint.

DESIGN AND LAMINATED WORK

Laminated work is used for making the framework of chairs and is also suitable for seats and backrests.

It is possible to make matching laminated stools providing that the function of the stool is clear and that the design is worked within the appropriate measurements.

THE UPRIGHT CHAIR

Hardwearing, strong, 'activity chairs' are ideal made from laminated wood. Some chairs in schools and offices are made from laminated frames, connected by cross rails with the thin laminated seats screwed and glued in place. Their light and springy construction, using continuously laminated members, avoid the strains which cause conventional joints to break. (See also *Chapter 8.*)

1960. Dining chair with one-piece laminated seat on chromium plated steel legs.

The resilience of thin laminations has made the use of unsupported, sculptured shapes possible. These 'one-piece' seats, which can be made on an open wood former (see *page 129*) and fixed onto metal legs, show the influence of pre-war experiments in the German Bauhaus.

THE EASY CHAIR

Although the Bauhaus designers used metal tubes for many chair designs, they recognised the springy quality of bent wood for making chair frames. The great strength and resilience of laminated frames can be used to make a chair which is both comfortable to sit in and attractive to look at.

Such constructions are light to move about and cause less damage to carpets than the conventional four-legged chair.

Similar frames are used to support upholstered seats—particularly for bedroom use.

Another use of laminated bends for easy chairs is in the making of rocking-chair rails.

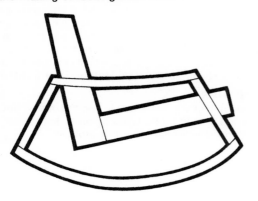

THE ROUND HIGH TABLE

Laminated bends used in the construction of pedestal tables, eliminate the traditional legs which can be awkwardly positioned on dining tables.

THE LOW TABLE

Low tables can be made with circuit laminations to support a variety of top surfaces.

A circuit lamination supports the glass top. The curved rails beneath connect the three legs and leave room for a nest of three small oval tables.

Constructions

These are basically simple. Glue and screws are used and bridle and halving joints are the most common.

Materials

The wood for frameworks is cut from sheets of veneer and plywood (1·5 mm thick).

Finishes

Both cellulose finished and polyurethanes are suitable for frameworks.

DESIGN **9** THE TELEPHONE UNIT

THE DESIGN PROBLEM

The invention of the telephone is comparatively new and its installation in the majority of homes is even more recent. The history, therefore, of the telephone table is only just beginning.

There is a four-fold problem of space involved in the design of such a table:

1. Space for the telephone
2. Space for writing messages
3. Storage for directories
4. Space for sitting

THE SOLUTION

The common solution is to put a seat next to a box containing the directories—a position which is inconvenient.

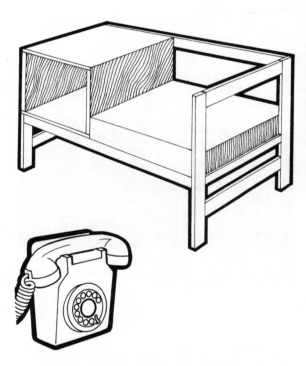

Such units are popular because they can be hung in working areas, such as the kitchen. Then there are only two design problems to solve, the storage of directories and space for writing messages.

The solutions will vary in size and proportion, depending on the wall space available but an important feature will be the need to fix the unit to the wall. (See *pp. 171–2.*)

It is essential to find out the measurements of the spaces required and relate these to the area in which the unit will go. Use scale elevations, experimenting with the different ways in which the spaces can be arranged.

Telephone:	200 mm × 125 mm × 125 mm
Message pad:	any size
Directories:	300 mm × 225 mm with their thickness and number depending on where you live.
Seat:	Minimum size 400 mm × 300 mm × 25 mm

One solution is to make the unit in the form of a desk. The seat is arranged so that the directories are easily accessible and the writing surface is at the correct height.

CONSTRUCTION

A leg and rail construction supporting a rectangular directory-storage box and square-edged upholstery, combine to make the unit neat in appearance. The design consists of a simple chair joined to the telephone table with a deep rail.

Suitable leg and rail joints are illustrated in section 44 and simple box joints in section 41.

Any hardwood is suitable for the frame and the directory-storage box can be of solid wood, veneered chipboard, or plywood. Consider a contrasting surface for the box top, e.g. a plastic laminate similar in colour to the seat cover, which will not mark in use. The upholstered cushion may be supported on a plywood base or on webbing which could be wrapped round the rail as a design feature. (See *Chapter 9.*)

FINISHES

Most finishes are suitable for the frame but the box top should be surfaced to resist hard wear and polyurethane would solve this problem.

EXAMINATION QUESTIONS

DESIGN

1. Design a stool with a cork top for use in a bathroom, considering the following points:

The stool will be in a steamy atmosphere and will often get wet.

A suitable height.

How you would support and fix the cork top.

Make as many preliminary sketches as you find necessary and then make a clear final freehand drawing of your design and:

(a) Give the main dimensions.

(b) Name the joints you would use.

(c) Show with a section how the cork top is fitted.

(d) Name a suitable finish. (MET)

2. Tools are very often carried in the boot of a car. These require a suitable container if they are to be kept in good order.

Plan, make and fit out such a container to hold the tools normally used on a car—but NOT the jacking equipment and wheel brace.

3. Show by means of a drawing and notes a design for a small pair of step ladders.

(a) The step ladders should be not more than five steps high and the maximum width of the steps should be 400 mm.

(b) Joints should be clearly shown.

(c) The following materials are available in the workshop and may be used as necessary:

Resin Glue   Screws   Nails

50 mm back-flap hinges

Parana pine. Boards planed to finish at 21 mm thick and 15 mm thick

4. Assume you have been given the responsibility to lead and organize a team of pupils to produce six bench garden seats for a Home for the Elderly. There is an ample selection of timber, fittings and finishing material at your disposal.

Explain and illustrate with free-hand drawings how you would set about designing the bench and how you would organize the production and assembling of six of these seats.

The following details should be given in your answer: (a) the factors influencing the design of the seat. (b) a free-hand drawing of a possible design for a bench seat. (c) the number of pupils required to make the seats and how you would organize the part to be played by each pupil. (MET)

5. Design and make a dining room trolley. The trolley should have two shelves. One shelf may be removable to form a separate tray.

6. Design a table or a stand to be used in your home to support a television set. The cabinet is veneered in Sapele Mahogany and has a natural (not highly polished) finish. Your answer should include the main dimensions, details of the joints of the timber used and the finish. (W)

7. A table is required at which to play chess. Make such a table to your own design. If desired the top may incorporate the chess board, but this is not essential.

8. Design a wall fixture to accommodate a telephone, the base of which measures 200 × 125 mm. Provide space for a writing pad and storage for two directories, each of which measures 400 mm × 300 mm × 19 mm. State the material and finish you would use. (S)

9. Design a small wall spice rack to hold ten jars giving the following information.

(a) The outside dimensions of the jars are 105 mm high and φ 45 mm.

(b) All jars are labelled as shown in the diagram, and must be clearly visible when placed in the rack.

(c) Wall fixing holes must be included. (WM)

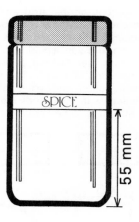

10. Design and make a small book-rack which could be used to hold about 20 paper-back books such as are published by Penguin.

11. Design a cage suitable for keeping guinea pigs or white mice. List the points which your design must fulfil and then make a freehand sketch to show the form the cage will take. (S)

12. A bench is needed to fit along one wall of a brick-built garage. The top of the bench is to be 2 m long by 450 mm wide.

Sketch a suitable design for the bench, add the measurements and make a cutting list of the timber needed. Make a pictorial sketch of the type of joint suitable for the underframing.

When finished the bench is to be fixed to the garage wall. Describe a suitable method of fixing and name the tools required to do the job.

13. Design a stand to hold four plant pots, each having a diameter of 90 mm and a height of 100 mm.

The design should ensure that:

(a) The pots are held in place and cannot be knocked on to the floor.

(b) The stand will remain firm on a flat surface.

(c) Drips of water will not run through after watering and spoil the window sill.

As many preliminary sketches as necessary may be made to develop the idea. Clearly indicate the final design by making a neat freehand drawing and:

(a) adding the principal dimensions,

(b) labelling the joints that will be necessary. (MET)

14. Design a simple but strong bicycle stand such as you might use for your own machine at home.

Your drawings may be in any form you wish, but should indicate clearly the dimensions, joints used, and the finish given to the wood. Add notes indicating the procedure you would follow in making this stand. (WM)

15. You have decided to make a timber attaché case to hold your football boots, strip and towel. Using notes and sketches, show how you would design and make the case. Mention the timber, type of glue, fittings and finish that you would use. (S)

16. Design a container to hold at least four shoe brushes and two tins of polish. The sizes of these items are given below and your solution should allow for easy access to them. Indicate in your notes where the container is to be kept.

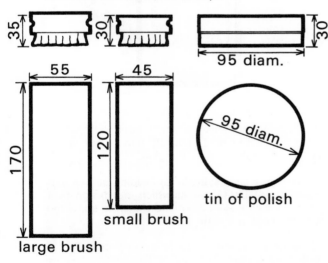

35

30

55

45

95 diam.

30

95 diam.

tin of polish

170

120

small brush

large brush

17. By means of freehand sketches and/or working drawings, design a small toboggan the maximum length to be not more than 1 metre. You must state the timber you propose to use, giving reasons, and any special finish to be applied.

Make clear drawings of ONE joint included in your design. (WM)

18. A toy consists of play blocks on the following modular system:

12 blocks 20 × 20 × 20
12 blocks 80 × 20 × 20
8 blocks 40 × 10 × 10
6 blocks 40 × 40 × 40

Design a container for these blocks that will provide for the following needs; *(a)* allow ease of removal and replacement of the blocks by a small child, *(b)* become part of the toy by providing opportunities for play in association with the blocks.

19. The photograph below shows a rocking toy. Use sketches and notes to show how you would construct it. List the materials and fittings. Design a suitable 'head' for it.

20. Name a small school job you have designed and describe how you made it using the following headings:

1. Make a large sketch about 100 mm long clearly showing main sizes and what the job looks like.
2. The important points you considered when designing it.
3. Materials required.
4. Finish.

21. Describe in detail the construction of the most pleasing piece of woodwork you have completed during your last two years at school. You must show one joint clearly, and name the timber used and the finish applied, giving reasons why these were particularly suitable for your job. (WM)

22. Write a short account of the design factors you would look for in judging the quality of a piece of modern furniture. Name the article, and refer to its appearance, finish, construction and utility. (JMB)

23. Choosing *either* (a) chairs *or* (b) tables, compare and contrast traditional constructional methods, using solid wood, with present-day methods of construction, using plywood or other new materials. (JMB)

24. How have modern machinery and industrial methods influenced the design and construction of furniture? Illustrate your answer.

94

MACHINE AND PORTABLE ELECTRIC TOOLS

6

The basic uses of the more popular machine tools are outlined in this chapter and the simplified illustrations will help you to understand how their controls are operated. A list of safety precautions, peculiar to each tool, will be found in every section.

GENERAL SAFETY

There are two important factors to remember to ensure general safety with machine tools:
1. The tools should be kept in good condition.
2. They should be used in the correct way.

Any power tool is capable of inflicting serious injury to both operator and bystanders if it is employed incorrectly or carelessly.

DO NOT USE ANY KIND OF POWER TOOL UNTIL YOU HAVE BEEN INSTRUCTED HOW TO OPERATE IT.

Unfortunately, whatever precautions are taken, accidents can and do happen. You should therefore be familiar with the position and use of the following:
● Emergency stop push-buttons or the isolating switch to turn off the electricity.
● A first-aid box.
● Fire-fighting equipment.

SPECIAL RULES TO OBSERVE

Be familiar with on-off switches.

Ensure that tools are properly plugged into supply sockets.

Treat cables with care.

Remove the plug from the supply socket or turn the isolating switch to 'off' before making adjustments to the machine.

Report any defects immediately.

Never tamper with the machine.

Do not interfere with the operator.

Only one person should operate a machine at any one time.

Protective clothing must be worn, e.g. an apron and face protection when necessary. (Aprons not only protect clothes from dirt and dust, but prevent loose clothing from being caught in moving parts.)

PROTECTION FROM FLYING PARTICLES

You should wear protective goggles or spectacles when using the lathe, the portable jigsaw and the sanding attachments. The best goggles can be worn over your own spectacles and are fitted with 'double glazing'. This is a double plastic lens which prevents steaming up and gives extra protection from flying wood or metal.

Some hardwoods e.g. Mansonia, when being sawn, turned or sanded, give off a most unpleasant dust. If you are troubled by dust, wear a filter mask. A fibre mask gives adequate protection, is not unpleasant to use and, being disposable, is hygienic.

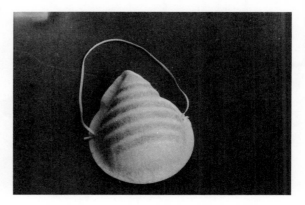

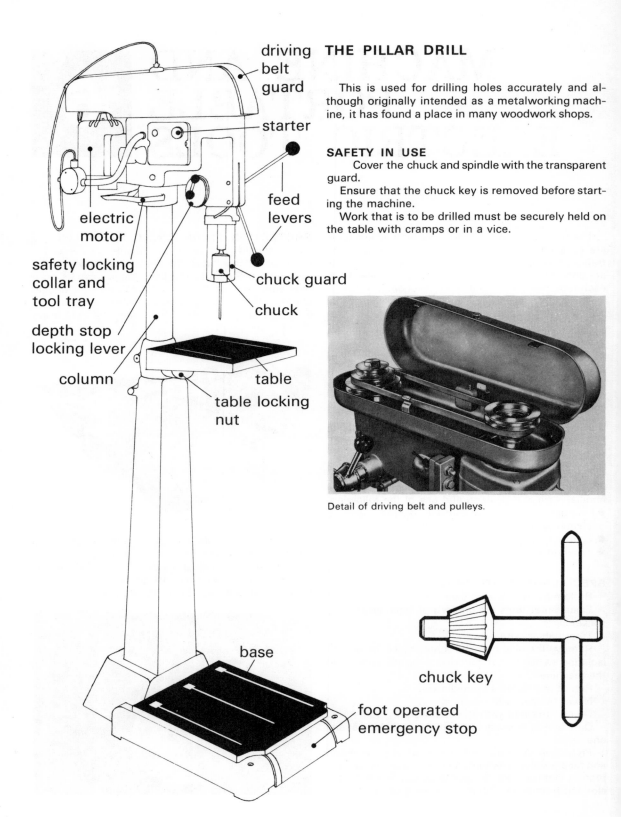

driving
belt
guard

starter

feed
levers

electric
motor

chuck guard

safety locking
collar and
tool tray

chuck

depth stop
locking lever

column

table

table locking
nut

base

chuck key

foot operated
emergency stop

Detail of driving belt and pulleys.

THE PILLAR DRILL

This is used for drilling holes accurately and although originally intended as a metalworking machine, it has found a place in many woodwork shops.

SAFETY IN USE

Cover the chuck and spindle with the transparent guard.

Ensure that the chuck key is removed before starting the machine.

Work that is to be drilled must be securely held on the table with cramps or in a vice.

WOOD-BORING BITS

Be sure to use a round-shanked bit of the size and type best suited to:
- the kind of timber to be bored
- the depth of the hole
- the diameter of the hole required.

The following bits are recommended:

For boring holes in hardwoods—a Scotch-nose pattern as shown in use.

Size guide: 12 mm diameter shank to bore holes 6 mm to 25 mm in diameter.

For boring holes in softwoods—a Jenning's pattern nose with plain bradpoint.

Size guide: 6 mm diameter shank to bore holes 6 mm to 38 mm in diameter.

For boring holes in plywood—a double-cutter machine centre-bit.

Size guide: 12 mm diameter shank to bore holes 6 mm to 75 mm in diameter.

Note: This bit cuts freely across or with the grain and will drill overlapping holes without 'running'. It is ideal for removing waste from work to be carved.

Scotch-nose pattern Jenning's pattern

For boring holes in chipboard—this presents special problems as the material varies so much in texture and the glue will quickly blunt normal bits. The use of tungsten-carbide tipped bits is recommended. On veneered chipboard, use a bit with spurs and stop when the drill tip protrudes at the back of the material. Finish drilling from that side.

When holes are bored into the edge of veneered chipboard, the sides should be supported.

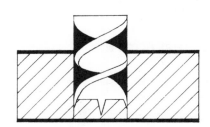

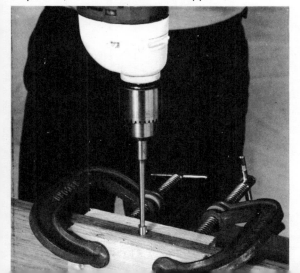

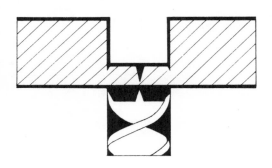

THE LATHE AND
LATHE APPLIANCES

The main uses of the lathe are:
- turning between centres
- faceplate turning
- long boring

In addition, a sanding attachment can be fitted.

Four speeds are generally available for the lathe, depending on the size of pulleys. They are in the region of 425, 800, 1400 and 2300 revolutions per minute (r.p.m.).

(See also *Chapter 7* on *TURNING* for details on the use of the lathe.)

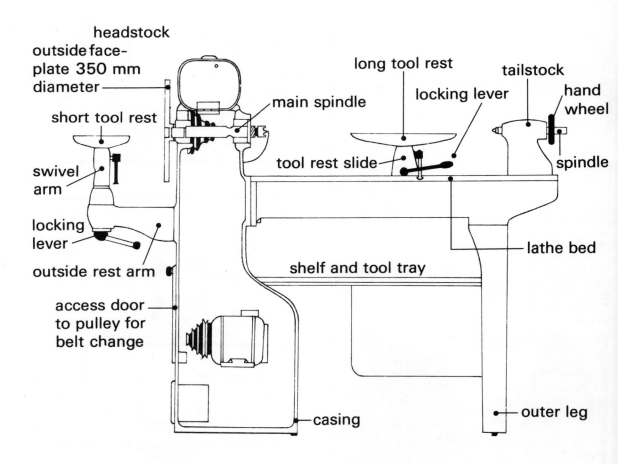

FACEPLATES

Outside faceplates with left-hand threads are used for turning work up to 500 mm diameter.

A plywood sanding pad, which can take 250 mm abrasive discs, may be screwed to the faceplate and used in conjunction with the sanding table.

Inside faceplates with right-hand threads are used for turning work up to 250 mm or 300 mm, according to the height of the spindle centre above the lathe bed.

Size guide: 75–350 mm diameter.

THE SCREWCHUCK

This is traditionally used for small diameter work but is not recommended for end grain work. The chuck is either a taper fit into the headstock spindle or is screwed onto it.

Size guide: 75–150 mm diameter.

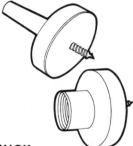

THE COIL CHUCK

The Child coil grip chuck has a screwchuck adaptor but normally uses a coil to grip end grain work such as jars, goblets and other 'holloware'. A reducing ring is available in which to hold small work.

Size guide: Up to the full capacity of the lathe.

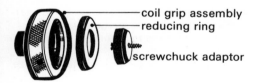

—coil grip assembly
—reducing ring

screwchuck adaptor

THE FORK CENTRE

The fork centre is used for driving light work to be turned between centres and is a taper fit into the headstock spindle. A four-prong chuck is available for heavy-sectioned timbers, e.g. table legs.

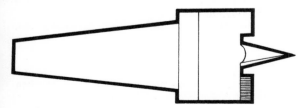

THE CONE OR TAPER CENTRE

This is a taper fit into the tailstock. It does not revolve with the work and is sometimes called the 'dead' centre. It is used for between-centre turning, and to support deep, faceplate work when the outside of the disc is being turned.

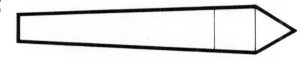

THE JACOB'S CHUCK

This will fit either the headstock or the tailstock spindle and will hold round-shank boring bits.

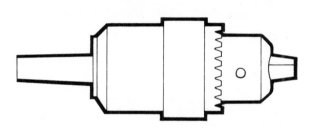

THE BOWL TURNING REST

It is not possible to have the straight tool rest close enough to the inside of a deep bowl for the work to be safe. An inside bowl turning rest is designed to suit curvature of most bowls. It can only be used with scraping tools and NOT with chisels or gouges.

THE LONG-BORING ATTACHMENT

The simplest type is a centre adapter which is pushed over the tailstock spindle and screwed down with a hexagonal key.

Size guide: To take Boring Augers of up to 9 mm diameter. (See *Woodwork 1, p. 121.*)

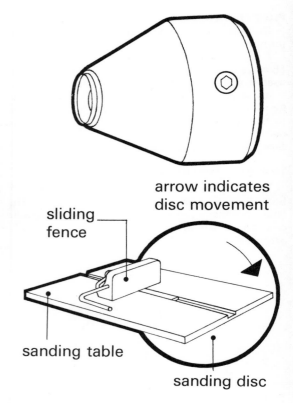

arrow indicates
disc movement

sliding
fence

sanding table

sanding disc

THE SANDING TABLE AND FITTINGS

The sanding table is fixed into the outside swive arm of the lathe and is fitted with a sliding fence. This has a simple length gauge and can be adjusted to any angle. It is used mainly for trimming ends of legs, mitre joints and dowelled butt joints.

It is essential that sanding is done only on the down-going side of the disc.

SAFETY IN USE

The general rules for the safe use of the lathe are:
One operator only.

Avoid loose clothing, particularly neckties.

Wear protective goggles or spectacles.

Use only suitable timber which has been properly prepared.

Secure work between centres or on a faceplate and have this checked before starting work.

Rotate the work by hand to make sure that it is free from obstruction.

Use a suitable speed for the type of material, size, and kind of job being turned.

Check that all levers are tight.

Use proper tools and make sure that they are a secure fit in their handles.

Do not measure work nor remove swarfe (waste) by hand, nor adjust the tool rest while the work is revolving.

Do not attempt to brake the work by hand; it is extremely dangerous.

Remove the tool rest before using abrasive paper.

Lathe sanding creates too much dust for comfort. This belt and disc sanding machine is fitted with a dust extractor unit.

THE CIRCULAR SAW

The circular saw, if properly maintained and used sensibly, saves invaluable time and energy in the preparation of materials.

Maximum depth of cut: 250 mm blade, 75 mm
                            300 mm blade, 100 mm

Its main jobs are: **ripping**
                    cross-cutting
                    mitring

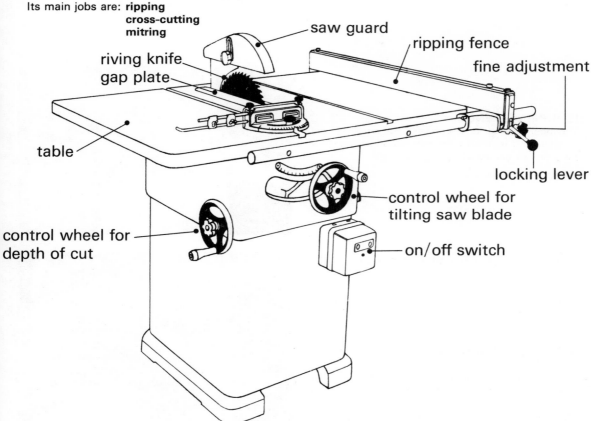

THE RIPPING BLADE

The teeth of the ripping blade have a positive hook and vary in size according to the diameter of the blade. The smaller teeth produce a smooth-sawn edge but the saw blunts more quickly. As a guide, the large teeth blades should be used on resinous softwoods and the smaller teeth on hardwoods.

THE CROSS-CUT BLADE

These teeth have a negative hook and are similar in appearance to the cross-cut teeth on a hand saw.

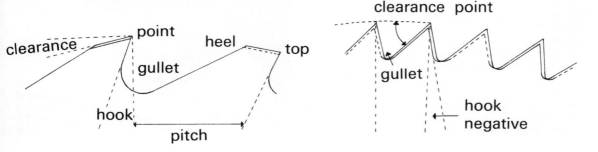

THE PLANER SAW BLADE

This blade is especially designed for cutting slabs of veneered plywood and chipboard. The cross-cut teeth make a scribing cut each side of the kerf and the rip-saw teeth remove the bulk of the waste.

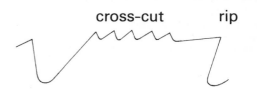

cross-cut   rip

THE RIPPING FENCE

The best type of fence runs the full length of the saw table and is fitted with a micro-adjustment for cutting timber accurately along its length.

THE CROSS-CUT AND MITRE FENCE

The fence slides in a groove, machined in the table top. It is calibrated in degrees, so that any angle can be cut, and when fitted with a simple length gauge, it is useful for repetition cross-cutting.

THE CIRCULAR SAW IN USE

The chipping of a surface is a hazard which can partly be avoided by lowering the saw blade so that it projects no more than 6 mm above the surface of the board.

Chipping on the top surface can be caused by the rising teeth as they pass through the kerf. This can be prevented by having a close-fitting riving knife which prevents contact between the wood and the rising part of the blade.

SAFETY IN USE

The machine should only be used by a qualified technician. If, however, you have access to a circular saw, observe the following safety regulations:

Check that the correct blade for the job is being used and that it is in good condition.

The riving knife must always be in position.

Use a suitable push stick to feed the last 300 mm of every cut, or with any shorter material when rip-sawing.

Do not attempt 'stopped' work—it is dangerous.

Take extra care when sawing thin timber.

Wear goggles or spectacles.

THE BANDSAW

Bandsaws are commonly used for sawing curves, although fences can be fitted for straight work. Cutting discs, ready for turning, and removing waste from shallow carvings are two of its uses. There are two main types of bandsaw, the two wheel and the three wheel. (See next page.)

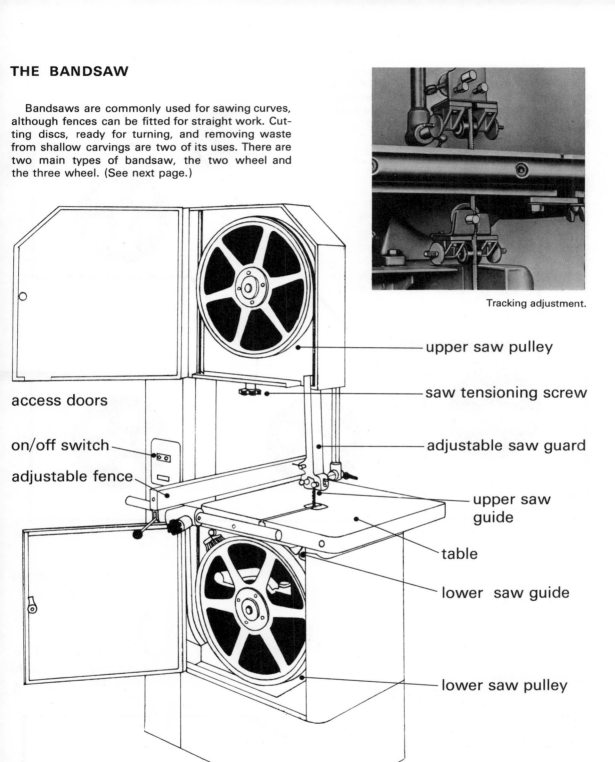

Tracking adjustment.

upper saw pulley

saw tensioning screw

access doors

on/off switch

adjustable fence

adjustable saw guard

upper saw guide

table

lower saw guide

lower saw pulley

footbrake

The difference in the two wheel and three wheel can be seen in the illustration. The depth of throat (A) must be less than the diameter of the wheels. The depth of throat (B) is restricted only by the size of the frame.

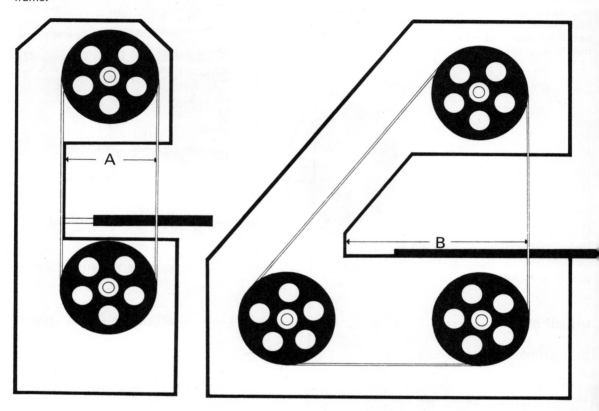

SAFETY IN USE

Use a blade of the correct size, 5–25 mm wide. It should be sharp and should not be distorted; these faults can cause breakage.

The blade must be properly guarded.

Tension the blade correctly but slacken off when not in use.

The top guide should be adjusted to the lowest possible position, as illustrated.

Fingers should be kept away from the saw line.

Stop the saw before making any adjustments.

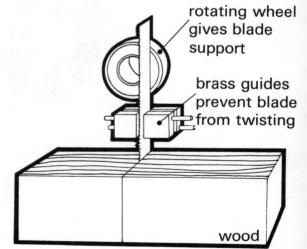

rotating wheel gives blade support

brass guides prevent blade from twisting

wood

THE ROUTER

The portable router will accommodate a wide variety of cutters that will groove, rebate and cut mouldings and chamfers.

The fast-rotating cutters give a clean cut in any grain direction, thus making the tool particularly useful on curved work.

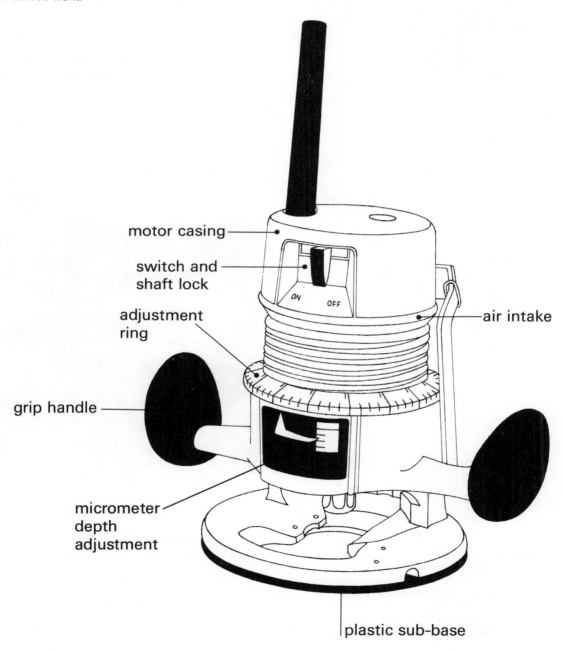

motor casing

switch and shaft lock

adjustment ring

grip handle

air intake

micrometer depth adjustment

plastic sub-base

ROUTER CUTTERS

The profiles illustrated indicate the variety of high-speed cutters available.

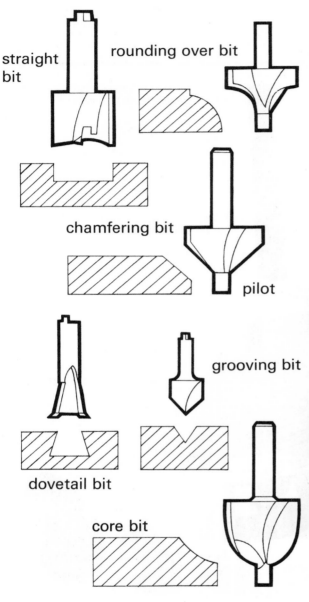

straight bit

rounding over bit

chamfering bit

pilot

grooving bit

dovetail bit

core bit

GROOVES

These can be of any width or depth. Grooves cut on board edges require extra support from battens in order to increase the bearing surface.

Housings cut across the grain have a wood guide cramped in position. Stopped housings will have round ends but these can be squared off with a chisel.

REBATES

These can be made on straight or curved work using the appropriate fence and straight cutter.

MOULDING AND CHAMFERING

This can be done with moulding cutters which are fitted with 'pilots' to follow the edge of the work, e.g. a table top. Chamfers are cut in the same way using an angled cutter.

SAFETY IN USE

Ensure that the cutter is secure in the collet chuck. Disconnect the motor before changing the cutter. Learn the correct method for adjusting the depth of cut.

Work being cut must be firmly held—holding devices must be well away from the line of cut.

Work from left to right for straight cutting and anti-clockwise on curved work. This will help the cutter to stay close to the work.

Feed at the correct speed, that is with the motor running without strain. This depends on:

(a) the cutter size
(b) the depth of cut
(c) the type of wood

Feeding too fast causes overloading. Feeding too slowly causes friction and possible damage to wood and cutter.

SANDING MACHINES

There are two main types of sanding machines:
- the belt sander
- the orbital sander

Both are designed to take the hard work out of finishing surfaces, particularly where large surface areas need sanding, e.g. in boat-building and on large cabinets.

THE BELT SANDER

This has a powerful motor, driving rollers on which an abrasive belt is tensioned. The model illustrated has a 100 mm wide abrasive belt, a vacuum bag and two speeds. The fast speed is for removing wood quickly and the slow speed is for removing varnish or for fine finishing.

The belt sander should only be applied to the work with the motor running at full speed. Move the machine back and forth with the grain, without applying extra pressure, overlapping the strokes to sand the surface evenly.

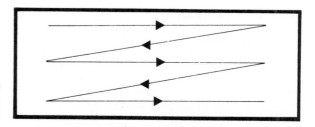

Keep the machine moving to prevent hollows, and avoid tilting as the belt will score the surface.

SAFETY IN USE

Do not switch on with the tool resting on the work—this may overload the motor.

Examine the abrasive belt before use—torn belts must not be used.

Disconnect the motor before changing the belt.

The arrow printed on the inside of the belt must point in the same direction as the arrows on the data plate.

Check tracking.

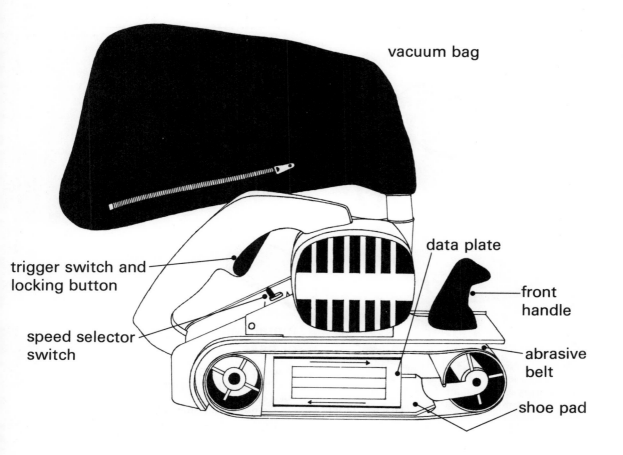

vacuum bag

trigger switch and locking button

speed selector switch

data plate

front handle

abrasive belt

shoe pad

107

THE ORBITAL SANDER

It is often referred to as a finishing sander because of the high quality of surface finish it can produce.

The model illustrated has a 200 × 100 mm foam-rubber pad glued to the metal base which rotates at about 5000 r.p.m. Using the correct abrasive sheets this produces a smooth, scratch-free surface.

When using the orbital sander, hold the handle firmly and switch on the machine before applying it to the work. Put the sander flat on the work and, using only light pressure, guide the machine over the surface with long, slow forward and back strokes. Do not apply undue pressure nor let the sander dwell in one spot.

ABRASIVE BELTS AND SHEETS

The grits are on paper, cloth or metal-backing sheets according to their type. There are also the 'Sandscreen' sheets for use with the orbital sander which consist of particles of silicon carbide, bonded to an open-weave material.

The best abrasives are:
- **Aluminium oxide**
- **Silicon carbide**
- **Tungsten carbide**

FAULTS IN ABRASIVES

Machine abrasives are subject to considerable friction which causes three major faults:

Loading or clogging—i.e. particles of surface lodged between abrasive grains. Check abrasive type and speed.

Stripping—breakdown of grains and bond. Check abrasive type and bonding.

Glazing—the abrasive grain loses its cutting edge and becomes dull. Check grade of abrasive.

The following abrasives are suggested to prevent these faults occurring. The degree of coarseness will depend on the work being done.

MATERIAL	BELT SANDER	ORBITAL SANDER
Hardwood	A.O. close	A.O. open
Softwood	A.O. open	A.O. open
Plywood	A.O. close	A.O. close
Blockboard	A.O. open	A.O. open
Chipboard	S.C. open	S.C. open
Hardboard	A.O. open	A.O. open
Plastic Laminate	A.O. close	A.O. close
Cork	S.C. open	S.C. open

A.O. = *Aluminium Oxide* S.C. = *Silicon Carbide.*

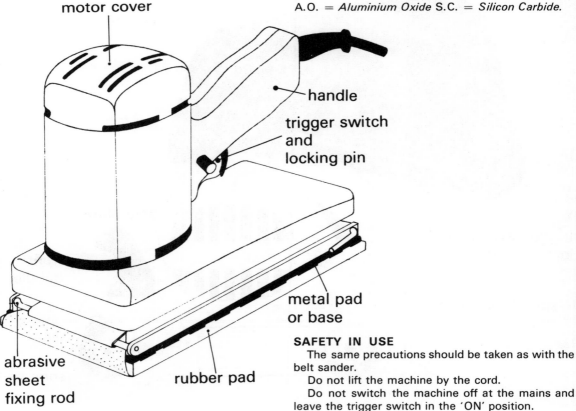

motor cover

handle

trigger switch and locking pin

metal pad or base

abrasive sheet fixing rod

rubber pad

SAFETY IN USE

The same precautions should be taken as with the belt sander.

Do not lift the machine by the cord.

Do not switch the machine off at the mains and leave the trigger switch in the 'ON' position.

THE JIG SAW

The portable jig saw is used for cutting curves in a variety of materials. It is particularly useful for sawing work, which is too large to cut on the bandsaw, and for removing internal waste as in a speaker cabinet. The model illustrated has an inbuilt air stream to keep the cutting line clear and, since it can make 2700 strokes per minute, will cut softwood up to 60 mm thick.

SAFETY IN USE

Disconnect the motor before changing blades.

Use the correct blade for the job to lessen the risk of breakage.

Check that the work is firmly held down and free from obstruction underneath.

Because of the upward-cutting action, wear protective goggles or spectacles.

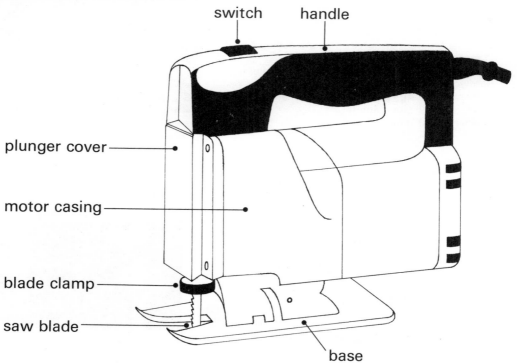

switch   handle

plunger cover

motor casing

blade clamp

saw blade

base

THE SAW IN USE

Take care to select the correct blade for the material to be cut. There are almost fifty different types to cover every job.

Wood blades—for all softwood work.

High-speed blades—for use on abrasive materials such as plywood, chipboard, plastics and some hardwoods.

Special blades—for steel, aluminium, building boards etc.

The saw is balanced for one-handed operation. The motor should be started before beginning the cut and should be fed forward. Do not slow the machine down—it will produce a rough cut and could break the blade. Because the saw has an upward-cutting action and veneered surfaces are liable to chip, it is best to mark out the shapes to be cut on the reverse side.

The portable jig saw being used to cut a shape from a sheet of plywood.

THE POWER UNIT

Power units are made in a wide range of sizes and capacities and although they may be similar in appearance, their performance will vary as much as that of a bubble car compared with the latest racing car.

A safe, reliable and adaptable unit would feature:
- two speeds, approximately 3000 r.p.m. and 900 r.p.m.
- double insulation for extra safety
- a 12 mm chuck to take all sizes of bits
- an automatic cut-out to prevent damage to the motor

Approximate drilling capacities for such a unit are:
Hardwood   32 mm diameter
Softwood   38 mm diameter
Steel   12 mm diameter
Masonry   19 mm diameter.

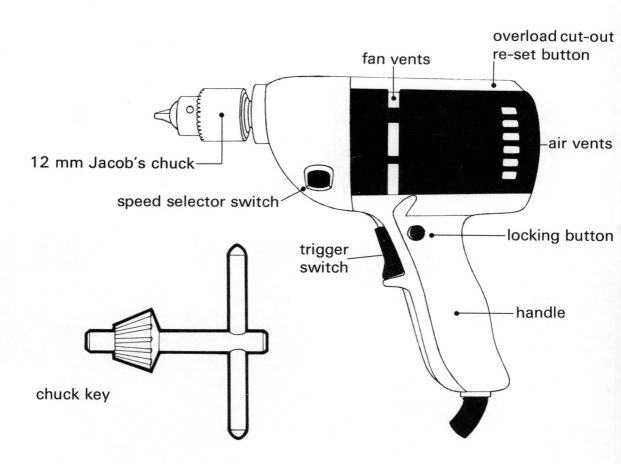

overload cut-out
re-set button

fan vents

12 mm Jacob's chuck

air vents

speed selector switch

locking button

trigger switch

handle

chuck key

SPECIAL WOOD-BORING BITS

Pilot holes to suit most screw gauges can be drilled with sharp twist drills. For repetitive work such as boat-building, a combined pilot, shank and countersink bit is useful. (See *Woodwork 1, p. 98*). The flat bit will bore holes quickly and accurately.

Note: The shank has three flats to ensure against slip in the chuck.

Size guide: 6—38 mm.

POWER UNIT ATTACHMENTS

There is a wide variety of attachments that can be fitted to power units but most attachments are not as convenient as a tool designed to do a particular job.

The Barrus 'Drillmate' is one example of a table-top drill stand which uses the power unit for precision drilling in wood, metal and plastics.

The power unit fits into a drill clamp and the work is supported on a work table which is bolted to the bench. A rack and pinion lever control ensures a positive feed into the work and a micro-adjustment setting and depth stop ensure a precise depth of cut.

The power unit is best employed for boring, but some abrasive attachments may be useful and safe to operate with it. These abrasives are attached to a hard, rubber backing-pad for coarse sanding.

The Barrus hand shaper attachment fits into a standard chuck and is safe to use for grooving, beading, cutting concave and convex radii and chamfering. A trimming cutter is ideal for plastic laminates and the 1·4 mm cutter makes slots to accommodate metal edging strips and extruded aluminium door handles.

The fence and drive shaft adjustment ensure vertical and horizontal accuracy of cut and the user's hand is safely shielded by the cutter guard.

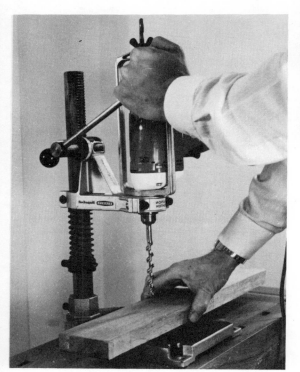

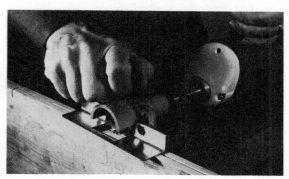

SAFETY IN USE

Although a number of woodworking attachments can be driven by a power unit, its main purpose is for use as a drill.

Cables to the power unit should be as short as possible. If the work cannot be taken near to an outlet socket, the cable should be suspended and dropped down at the working position.

Disconnnect the motor before changing the bits.

Use only bits designed for machine work.

Secure work to be drilled.

Ensure that the chuck key is removed before starting the machine.

Hold the power unit with both hands.

Note: A side handle is useful for heavy work.

EXAMINATION QUESTIONS

MACHINE AND PORTABLE ELECTRIC TOOLS

1. A friend has borrowed your power unit to drive his rotary lawn mower. Make a list of the safety checks you would make when the unit is returned to you.

2. Why are there several speeds on a lathe?

3. Write an account of the safety precautions which should be observed before switching on the power to start a lathe. Use the following headings.
(a) A safe method of mounting the work on a face-plate when making a bowl.
(b) The position of the tool rest.
(c) Personal safety (eyes, hands and clothing).

4. Name FOUR safety precautions which should be observed before and while using a circular saw.

5. Precautions are taken in the workshop for the safety of:
(a) the user of a tool;
(b) the user of a machine;
(c) the other occupants of the workshop;
(d) the tools and machines.
Give two examples of possible danger under each of these four headings, and state what precautions you would take to avoid these dangers.

6. Many workshops possess power tools both portable and fixed, such as drills, lathes, saws etc.
Write notes about the safe operation of TWO portable power tools you have used, listing possible dangers, together with necessary safety precautions you should observe. (WM)

6. There were 19,000 personal accidents reported by industrial and commercial managements during the year 1969, many of which could have been avoided by taking more care and using a little fore-thought. Under the following headings mention any important safety rules and precautions which apply to workshops.
(a) Moving about the workshop.
(b) Making a large plate on the lathe. Show the method of securing the work.
(c) The choice and use of a hammer.
(d) Sawing a board which is held in the bench vice.
(e) The design of tool racks and workshop equipment.

8. You have hired a belt sander from a local shop to sand your dining room floorboards. On checking the machine you discover that the plug is cracked and must be replaced.
Make notes to describe how you would wire up a 3 pin 13 amp plug to; (a) three-core cable, (b) two-core cable, (c) cable with wires coloured black, red and green.

9. You have a workshop at the rear of the garage which has no natural light. Copy the plan given and on it show the position of; (a) work surfaces, (b) a saw bench, grinding wheel and drill stand, (c) lights and power sockets.

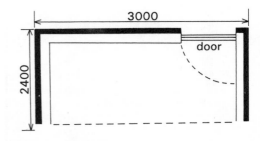

10. A transformer is often used between the power supply and a powered hand-tool. What job does it do?

TURNING

INTRODUCTION

The information in this section and the notes on the lathe in Chapter 6 are intended as a source of reference for the basic turning that is required for the average job.

The section describes:
- (a) Turning between centres
- (b) Faceplate turning

Details of more specialised forms of the craft will be found in books especially written for the wood turner.

TURNING TIMBERS

It is possible to turn almost any type of timber on the lathe but hardwoods can usually be given a better finish than softwoods. The list of timbers below is a guide to the materials most likely to be available, although stocks of turning woods vary. The timbers are divided into four groups to show their comparative cost.
1. Expensive timber.
2. Timbers not easy to obtain, usually expensive.
3. Medium-priced timber.
4. Lower-priced timber.

Note: An expensive wood does not necessarily turn better than a cheaper variety.

Unless otherwise stated, the wood is available in planks—150—300 mm wide, or turnery discs—150—275 mm diameter, and in each case the usual maximum thickness is given.

Special uses other than for decorative work, bowls etc. are listed.

1 EXPENSIVE TIMBER

Afrormosia (75 mm) A hard brown timber with a variable grain.

Mahogany Honduras, (100 mm) Close-grained, deep-red, even colour. Turns and finishes well with a high shine. Large decorative bowls. Detailed work.

Oak Plain Japanese, (50 mm) Open-grained, light-coloured wood. Mild working.

Oak Quartered Japanese, (100 mm) The medullary figuring is not as strong as in English Oak. It will turn well and stay flat and is suitable for large bowls.

Teak (100 mm) The larger diameters (over 200 mm) of this attractive brown timber are not always available. The abrasive grain quickly blunts tools. Salad bowls, legs.

Walnut, European (100 mm) Attractive, smooth-surfaced wood which turns and polishes well. High class and detailed work. Jars, egg-cups, serviette rings etc.

2 TIMBER, NOT EASY TO OBTAIN

Lignum Vitae Noted for its extreme denseness. It turns well with sharp tools. Carvers' mallets, bowling 'woods', detailed work.

Rosewood The wood is usually only available in small quantities. It is often badly split and this means it comes in small sizes and small squares. Sold by weight. All types of small decorative work. Drawer pulls.

Yew An English softwood with a hard, attractive pink grain. The characteristics which make it an excellent carving material also make it ideal for turning.

3 MEDIUM-PRICED TIMBER

Beech (75 mm—maximum width 200 mm) Close, even grain that will turn well and give an excellent finish. Stains evenly. Chair-making, handles, kitchenware.

Cherry (50 mm) A pink, close-grained wood that turns well. Supplies are limited. Suitable for chair-making.

Chestnut (100 mm) Similar to Oak in appearance but it is without the figuring and is cheaper.

Elm, English (100 mm) The open, wild grain is attractive when used for faceplate work—large widths available.

Elm, Japanese (75 mm) Lighter in both weight and colour than the English variety. Turns and stains well.

Iroko (100 mm) An African wood similar in colour to Teak and quite durable. Hard and open-grained but takes a good finish.

Maple (75 mm) A hard, pale close-grained wood which turns well. Used for billiard cues.

Olive (75 mm) An uncommon wood. Yellow-brown in colour with deep streaky markings and a smooth finish.

Walnut, African (75 mm) An attractive, golden-brown wood with dark streaks. Large sizes can be obtained.

Zebrano (100 mm) A pinkish wood, with irregular purple-brown streaks, which looks best on faceplate work.

4   LOWER-PRICED TIMBER

Agba (75 mm) Straight, mild grain; pinkish-brown in colour. Turns cleanly but lacks interest. Small diameter work.

Ash (100 mm) A tough, light-coloured wood with 'elastic' qualities. Used for cricket stumps and bails, tool handles, croquet mallets etc.

Lime (100 mm) Light-coloured and mild. Cuts well on the lathe as it does when being carved.

Mahogany, African (100 mm) Both colour and texture are variable. Lighter varieties will stain well but the surface is often soft.

Plane or Lacewood (100 mm) A strong, pale-coloured timber. Large sizes are liable to twist.

Utile (100 mm) A red African wood often with a twisted grain. Difficult to finish well.

Sapele (100 mm) A hard, close-grained wood, similar to many mahoganies but paler in colour. Large diameters possible.

Sycamore (100 mm) Close, even grained. It is hygienic in use and suitable for bread and chopping boards, rolling pins etc.

CHOOSING TIMBER

Turnery discs can be obtained, cut to size with a bandsaw and sealed on the edge with paraffin wax, but it is cheaper if you cut your own disc from a well-seasoned plank.

Example of cost: Timber for an Elm bowl 200 mm to 225 mm diameter and 75 mm thick (1978 prices).

    From a plank £1.00
    From a turnery disc £1.50

FAULTS IN TIMBER

For between centre work, squares of timber that are misshapen, and planks of timber that are warped, can be used with safety. It is some indication that the timber has dried out and that subsequent movement of the timber is less likely to occur. (See *Woodwork 1, p. 30.*)

Top right
Sugar bowls in yew and lime, both with surface faults that have been filled in.

Right
From left to right, maple, teak, elm and zebrano.

Turnery discs become oval in shape when they dry out. For example, the Maple bowl in the photograph measured 200 mm along the grain and 192 mm across the grain, before turning.

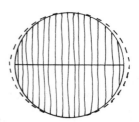

End splits and short grain must be avoided but small surface checks are rarely a problem.

Shakes in thicker material do not always mean that the wood is unsuitable—many can be turned out if the right shape can be designed.

Note: If the wood is unusable, do not throw it away. Carve it.

WOOD-TURNING TOOLS

These tools can be divided into two groups—those with a **cutting action** and those with a **scraping action**.

CUTTING TOOLS

Gouges These are used for shaping the wood to size and, with experience, for good finishing on curved surfaces. Work between centres and the convex outside of bowls is shaped with a gouge, ground square across. A round-nose gouge is used for working hollows, e.g. the inside of bowls.

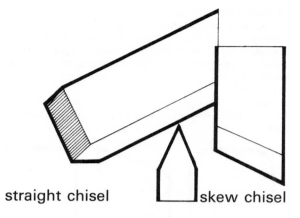

straight chisel · skew chisel

Chisels When used correctly, they produce both straight and convex surfaces which require a minimum of sanding. The chisel may be sharpened square across or at an angle of about 70°. It is then called a skew chisel.

The Parting Chisel This is a deep chisel used for cutting shoulders and finishing to length work which is turned between centres, e.g. stool legs. The chisel is tapered back from the cutting edge so that it does not bind.

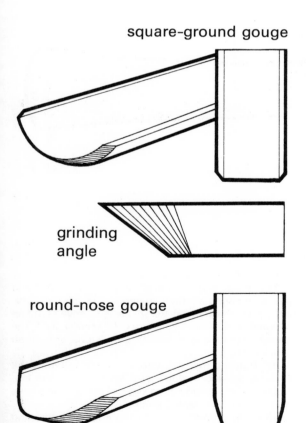

square-ground gouge

grinding angle

round-nose gouge

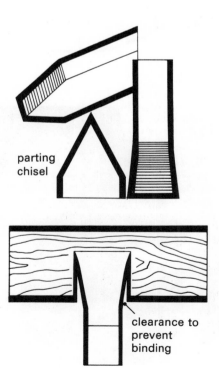

parting chisel

clearance to prevent binding

SCRAPING TOOLS

Specially tempered scraping tools are sold, but they can also be made by grinding down old files. Only very thick files should be used as thin files are liable to break. The top of the scraper is top ground at a slight angle and the grinding angle need not be less than about 60°.

Because scraping tools are cheap to make, most workshops have a variety of shapes and sizes available.

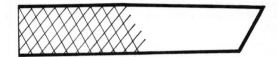

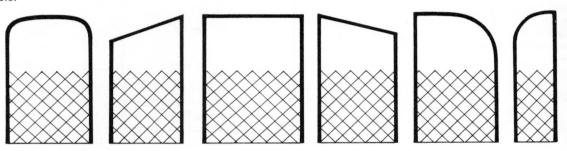

LATHE TOOL HANDLES

These are longer than bench chisel handles to enable sufficient leverage to be obtained. They are made from Ash.

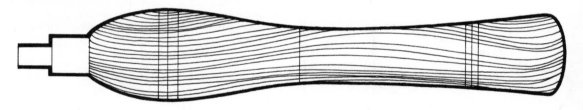

SHARPENING LATHE TOOLS

The gouge is ground at an angle of about 30° and has no separate sharpening angle. Like a firmer carving gouge the burr on the inside is removed with an oilstone slip. (See *Woodwork 1, section 27*.) The gouge may be sharpened on an oilstone or with an oilstone file.

Note: Rocking the tool across a stone will mark the surface, so use a stone kept specially for the job.

Chisels are ground at an angle of 20° and also have no separate sharpening angle.

The burr produced on the top edge of a scraping tool, when grinding, is left on. This gives the tool a 'cutting' edge.

TURNING BETWEEN CENTRES

Turning between centres describes the process whereby the wood is mounted between the headstock and the tailstock of a lathe, parallel to the lathe bed. (See *Chapter 6, p. 98.*)

More than three centuries ago, the hardwood chair shown opposite was turned by a craftsman using similar skills to those needed by you to turn the more familiar stool legs, lamp bases, table-lamp columns and, on a smaller scale, drawer knobs.

TURNING A STOOL LEG

PREPARING THE WOOD
1. Select wood with straight grain and cut to length.
2. Mark diagonals on each end to find the centre, then scribe a circle.
3. Use a pencil to mark off tangents to the circle and finger gauge along the length.
4. Remove the waste with a jack plane—the wood is held in a cradle.
5. Centre-punch each centre, then make a shallow saw cut across one end. Tap the fork centre with a mallet into this end, then mount the work on the lathe.

Lightly oil or grease the cone centre in the tailstock. Check that there is no side movement and that work will revolve easily.
6. For scraping, position on the long tool-rest slightly below the centre of the work (as close as possible without touching) and check for clearance.
7. Select the speed. A fast speed can be used for small diameter work, i.e. 1300 to 1400 r.p.m.

SCRAPING
Use a round-nose scraper, first to turn the wood into a cylinder, then to shape the taper. Finish with a flat-nose scraper. Hold the scrapers in a horizontal position or with the handle slightly raised.

CUTTING
Raise the tool-rest slightly above centre and roughly shape the cylinder with a gouge. The ribbed surface produced is removed by turning the gouge on to its side and drawing it in either direction along the rest.

(Crown Copyright, Victoria and Albert Museum)

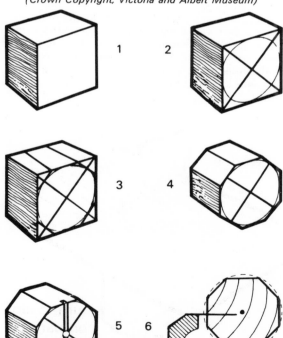

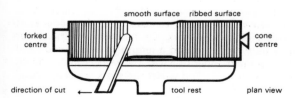

smooth surface   ribbed surface

forked centre

cone centre

direction of cut   tool rest   plan view

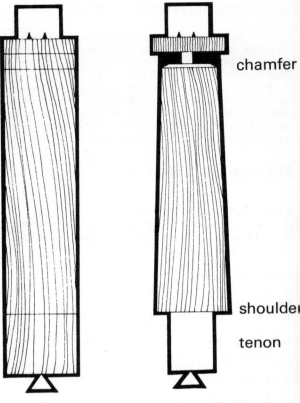

chamfer

shoulder

tenon

The bottom of the leg is chamfered before the work is removed from the lathe.

For final shaping with a skew chisel, the bevel of the chisel is laid on the work and the handle raised slightly to make the chisel cut. Work from the centre to the outside of the work, cutting with the heel and taking care not to catch the work with the chisel point. *Note:* With cutting and scraping tools, aim to produce 'ribbon' shavings.

Mark the tenon shoulder and the length of the leg with a pencil. Use a parting tool to cut on the waste side of each line, then turn the tenon to size. *Note:* At frequent intervals, check with calipers the diameter of the leg and the diameter of the tenon to ensure a perfect fit into the stool base or under-frame.

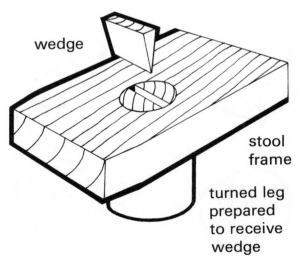

wedge

stool frame

turned leg prepared to receive wedge

FINISHING

Ideally, work can be finished straight from the chisel but usually some sanding is necessary. Fill small holes with a proprietary filler that will not be affected by the final polish. Rough patches on the work suggest that the tool is blunt or that the lathe speed is too slow.

The fast speeds used for finishing work off cause glass-paper and garnet paper to be quickly blunted and burned. Aluminium Oxide paper (open coat) is recommended, using nothing coarser than 80 and working down to 180, (see *Woodwork 1, page 188*). The tool-rest must be removed and the paper kept moving along the work. On flat surfaces the paper may be wrapped round a length of waste wood and used in the manner of a file. The work is dusted down and the finish applied whilst the work is still mounted on the lathe.

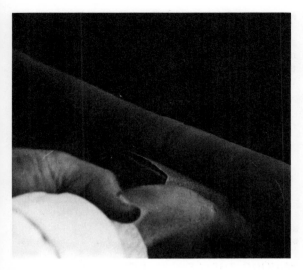

FINISHES

Quick-drying cellulose, one of the many polyurethane finishes, or an acid-catalysed lacquer would be suitable. (See *Woodwork 1, pp. 103—4.*)

Brush or French polish is somewhat outdated and is now generally only used as a sealing coat before the application of Teak oil.

Finally, saw off the remaining waste and smooth on the disc-sander attachment. (See *Chapter 6.*)

TURNING A TABLE-LAMP COLUMN

A table-lamp column is prepared and turned in the same way as a stool leg but it is necessary to drill a hole for the lamp flex.

The conical centre in the tailstock is removed and replaced by the long-boring centre attachment. (See *Chapter 6 p. 100.*)

A boring auger is fed through the hollow tailstock into the work, boring beyond half way. The column is then reversed and the procedure is repeated until the centre hole is complete. (For details of the boring auger see *Woodwork 1, p. 121.*)

FACEPLATE TURNING

This is a method of turning for producing mainly bowls and dishes, although the base of the table-lamp column described in the previous section will also be turned in this way.

TURNING A TABLE-LAMP BASE
PREPARING THE WOOD

1. The base will probably be no more than 150 mm diameter by 25 mm thick and can be cut from a suitable board.
2. Select the less attractive side, which will be the bottom, and plane it flat.
3. On the planed side, mark the diagonals and draw a circle equal to the diameter of the faceplate being used. (A)
4. Mark the tangents to the circle with a pencil and remove waste wood with a cross-cut saw. (B) (Hold the wood on a sawing trestle with a G-cramp.)
Note: Use a bandsaw or portable sabre saw if available.

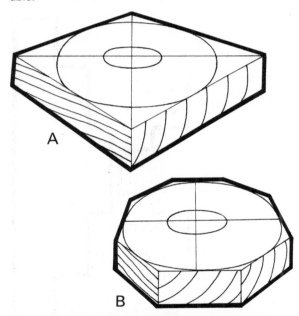

A

B

MOUNTING THE WORK

It is possible to screw the faceplate directly on to the wood, but in this case, because the work is shallow and a centre hole has to be bored, a piece of softwood is sandwiched between the wood and the faceplate. The piece of softwood, about 15 mm thick, is prepared and fixed to the faceplate with heavy screws, usually 25 mm, No 10 or 12, and turned down to the diameter of the faceplate. The wood to be turned is then glued to this disc, using a PVA adhesive, with a piece of paper between the wood and the disc. This makes subsequent removal easier.

Note: The grain of the softwood disc is set at right angles to the grain of the wood to be turned.

The assembly is set up on the headstock using a leather washer to prevent the faceplate from tightening itself onto the spindle during turning.

The T-rest is positioned slightly below centre, as close as possible to the work, without touching, and checked for clearance. The work is not large and the second slowest speed can be used—about 900 r.p.m.

METHOD OF TURNING

When the block is glued and not screwed it is advisable for less-experienced workers to use the scraper only. A skew scraper is used, working from the face of the work, to turn the block into a cylinder. This is then shaped with a round-nose tool.

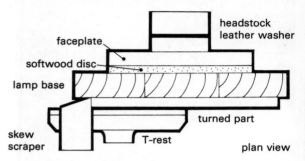

MAKING THE CENTRE HOLE

The hole for the lamp column is accurately bored with a suitable bit. The bit is mounted in a Jacob's chuck in the tailstock and fed into the work. (See *Chapter 6, p. 99.*) The base should be polished whilst in position on the lathe. It is separated from the softwood block by inserting a large chisel in the glueline and tapping it sharply with a mallet. The surface may be scraped clean and polished or be covered with a protective material before the lamp is finished.

Note: After the work is glued up, a small diameter hole for the flex is bored through the radius of the base.

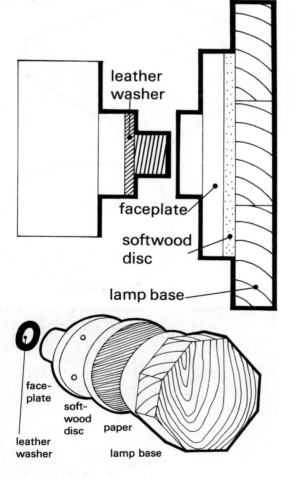

TURNING A BOWL

PREPARING THE WOOD

The wood is prepared in the same way as for the table-lamp base but, being thicker material, generally 60 to 100 mm, it can be screwed directly to the face-plate. It is common practice to turn the outside and base of a bowl and then to reverse it to hollow out, but the problem of re-centring the wood is eliminated if a faceplate is used which is slightly smaller than the intended base of the bowl.

Note: Check the length of the screws before mounting the block. They should go into the block a distance of between 12 mm and 19 mm depending upon the thickness of the timber and diameter of the bowl.

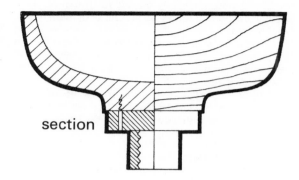

section

PREPARATION AND MOUNTING

A third way to hold faceplate work is to use the expanding collet chuck.

This is only one of the six functions which can be performed by the Universal chuck, and it does have the advantage of not using screws. This enables it to be used safely for large diameter work, and bowls can be cut deeper without the danger of hitting screws.

Using a standard faceplate (or the Universal chuck as a faceplate) turn the bowl into a cylinder.

On the face turn a flat recess with a scraper, exactly 88 mm in diameter and 6 mm deep. Under-cut or 'dovetail' the recess with a skew chisel.

Reverse the wood on to the collet chuck with the collets close together.

Tighten the screw ring and, with a large pin spanner, nip the dovetail tight so that it is ready to use.

The work is mounted as before, the T-rest being positioned at right angles to the work, parallel to the lathe bed, and about centre.

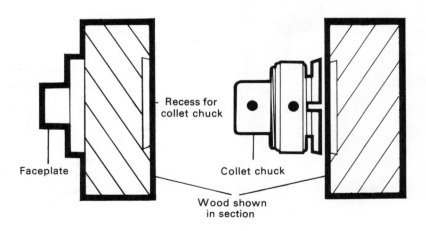

Faceplate

Recess for collet chuck

Collet chuck

Wood shown in section

121

METHOD OF TURNING

Turning a cylinder from the edge is an alternative to the method previously described. It can be done equally well with a round-nose scraper or more quickly with a cutting gouge. The gouge is more likely to dig into the work if it is not used correctly and for the inexperienced woodworker it is good practice to remove some of the material with a gouge and to finish with a scraper.

If a round-nose gouge is used, the bevel should be rested on the work, and the tool turned and pulled across the work with only the side of the edge cutting. The outside shape is turned first before hollowing out.

HOLLOWING OUT

This is quickly done with the round-nose gouge but even experienced turners prefer to use a scraper to finish off.

Start by turning a hollow in the centre of the bowl, then enlarge it until the basic shape is achieved.
Note: Occasionally check the depth of the hollow to avoid the faceplate screws.

If the base of the hollow is flat, it can be finished with a flat scraper and the curved sides merged into it.

It is not uncommon to experience patches of rough grain at opposite sides of the bowl on the end grain. To remove these, sharpen the scraper, increase the spindle speed and make a very light cut before sanding the surface smooth.

The bowl is then given a suitable finish.

Note: If the work is screwed to a normal faceplate check the depth of the hollow to avoid hitting the screws.

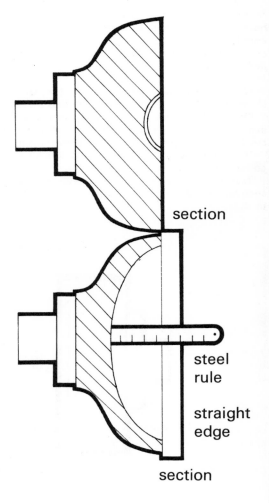

section

steel rule

straight edge

section

THE USE OF TEMPLATES

These are needed when work has to be of an exact shape or when more than one piece of the same shape has to be produced, e.g. candle-holders. Normally, however, a working drawing can be followed by 'eye' and if the finished result is not exactly as intended but looks and feels good, then the bowl is quite satisfactory. For most work, exact size is not particularly important either and the use of calipers is restricted to repetitive work or, for instance, when a lid has to be fitted onto a bowl.

DESIGNING FOR LATHE WORK

The most successful designs are basically simple in outline, allowing the natural beauty of the timbers, as they are turned, to show to advantage. To produce items of work which are beautiful does not necessarily mean that you have to be clever in using the lathe, although the ability to turn a set of chessmen is a useful asset.

A grasp of the basic techniques and a sense of form will be of most value. Much of the intricate work done on lathes shows considerable skill but the quality of wood is lost and such examples are more suitably made from a less interesting material, e.g. metal or plastic. If you are unable to obtain wood with an interesting grain, then the *shapes* that you design will have to provide the points of interest.

Three sugar bowls based on the square and circle and made in attractive English oak.

Colour, pattern and texture may be applied to make the design more attractive. In addition to the more obvious textured surfaces, e.g. coloured hessian or linen, make use of vinyl wallpaper offcuts to match your room decorations.

Note: Where a geometric pattern is used, the objects should be made the exact size required. This involves planning. Never add decoration to your work but plan it as part of the original idea.

If your efforts at bowl-turning occasionally meet with a slight accident, for example when an edge may be thin and break off, finish the rest of the bowl. Remove the work from the lathe and, holding the faceplate in a vice, use a round-faced spoke-shave to hollow opposite 'sides'. The result is particularly attractive with deep bowls.

Lathe work is also used as a means of displaying and supporting various mechanisms such as clocks, barometers and table-lighters. It is often possible to give a new look to second-hand mechanisms.

Once confidence is gained in the use of the lathe, you will be able to design and make children's toys and play shapes. Toys made from plain timber—Beech is a good example—can be given a smooth finish and painted with chip-free lacquers. The occasional spare 'hour' can be occupied with this type of work and otherwise 'wasted' short ends of wood can be used up.

EXAMINATION QUESTIONS
TURNING

1. Why does a lathe have a pulley system that enables one to select different turning speeds? Include in your answer a sketch or diagram of a pulley system that will give three speeds indicating the pulleys driven by the motor. Give an example of what could be turned when each of the outer pairs of pulleys are used.

2. You have to produce **four** taper turned legs to the measurements indicated in the drawing below. These legs are to be turned from 50 mm × 50 mm beech 410 mm long. Describe fully, together with illustrations, the procedure you would work through to complete these legs up to and including final polishing.

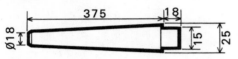

3. The drawing below shows one of a set of turned skittles made from a piece of 50 mm × 50 mm hardwood. Describe how you would prepare the timber for turning, set the wood up in the lathe, and ensure that the skittles are the same shape.

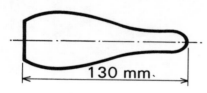

4. Design and make a fixed or adjustable standard lamp which includes some turned work. Your final solution could involve the use of metal tubing for the stem. (If you select a metal stem, make sure that earthing has been taken care of.)

5. A ladder rung suitable for a climbing frame is shown below. Describe by sketches and notes how you would turn the rung from a length of 40 mm × 40 mm Ash. Include in your answer details of:
(a) the preparation of the wood ready for the lathe;
(b) the method of mounting the wood in the lathe;
(c) turning the overall diameter;
(d) reducing the diameter of the ends.

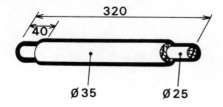

6. The drawing shows the shape of a small, round, hardwood bowl or dish. Describe how you would turn it, using the following headings:
(a) Preparation and mounting of the wood in the lathe—use notes and sketches.
(b) Turning—give details of each step and name the tools used.
(c) Finishing—suggest a suitable finish and the method of applying it.

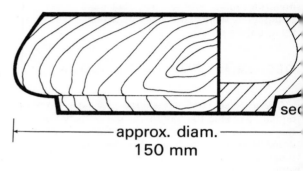

approx. diam.
150 mm

7. Describe how to set up and turn the inside of a shallow plate with special attention being given to the method of securing and centring and how it is checked to ensure that it conforms to the designed shape.

8. Design and make a frame for a circular mirror of 125 mm diameter. (W)

9. You are required to produce a salt pot and a pepper pot on the lathe. Design a suitable shape. Your free hand drawings should show a cross section along the length of each pot and all the important dimensions. Give a brief but detailed account of the stages required to produce each pot using the following headings as a guide: (a) preparation of wood; (b) method of mounting and setting on the lathe; (c) shaping the outside; (d) removing wood from the inside; (e) marking out and drilling a single hole for the salt pot; (f) marking out and drilling a number of holes for the pepper pot; (g) fitting a stopper; (h) cleaning up and finishing. (MET)

10. You have made a small cabinet complete with a door and a drawer and need two handles for it.
(a) Make a freehand pictorial sketch of a suitable shape for a handle which has to be turned on the lathe. State the sizes.
(b) Write detailed notes on the stages in the turning, finishing and polishing of the handles.
(c) Make a sketch showing a method of fixing the handles to the door and drawer front.

LAMINATING AND BENDING

INTRODUCTION

Laminating is the process by which wood is built up, layer by layer, to produce a length or cross-section of material greater than that which can be economically obtained from a log.

Note: The process is not confined to wood.

EXAMPLES OF LAMINATION

1. **Plywood** and **blockboard slabs**; these are only restricted in size by the capacity of the machines that manufacture them.

2. **Laminated bends** for furniture and musical-instrument making are built up from any number of veneer strips glued together, with the grain running in the same direction. When the glue sets, the thin layers are permanently formed and have great strength.

3. **Laminated beams** consist of standard timber lengths, glued together in the same way as the veneers used in furniture-making. They have become an important feature of modern building techniques. Softwoods, glued with suitable resin adhesives, can be made to span most buildings and can also be bent. (See *Woodwork 1, p. 36.*)

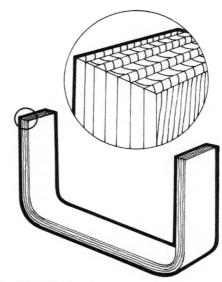

END JOINTING

For lengths that are greater than the material being used, end jointing is necessary. The scarf joint, used in the early days of laminating, not only wastes timber but it is difficult to glue up. The latest machine method uses a tapered finger joint. The finger joint can also be marked out with a template and cut by hand.

The strength of the beam will depend upon the accuracy with which the joint is cut and fitted.

Note: This method can also be used for joining lengths of solid wood used in traditional construction work.

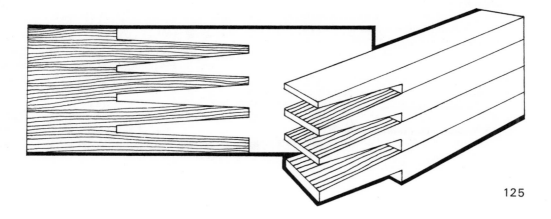

TIMBERS USED

Cheap softwoods are normally used for straight laminations and, if necessary, the construction is covered with decorative hardwood lippings and veneers.

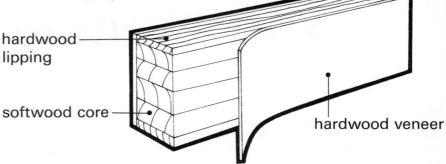

hardwood lipping

softwood core

hardwood veneer

Curved laminations are made with timbers having natural bending properties. The best of these are the English timbers Ash, Beech, Elm and Oak. Veneers of any type can be used but the large number of strips needed and the extensive gluing area make the work expensive. Sheets of constructional veneer, specially for laminating, can be bought and cut to size with a saw, knife and straight edge or a cutting gauge. These are used as cores with a more attractive veneer glued on to the surfaces.

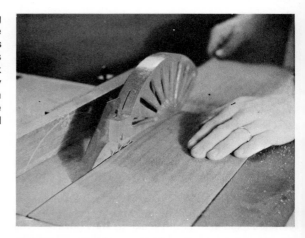

Constructional veneer being cut on a circular saw.

ADHESIVES FOR LAMINATION

Select an appropriate adhesive for the situation in which the work will stand—for example, outdoors or indoors. With the correct adhesive, the large gluing areas within the work will ensure adequate strength.

Suggested adhesives:

Permanent outdoor use—R.F. resin
e.g. *Aerodux 500* or *Cascophen*

Occasional outdoor use: U.F. resin
e.g. *Aerolite 306* or *Cascomite 'One-Shot'*

Indoor use: P.V.A. or Casein types
e.g. *Evo-stik Resin 'W'* or *Cascomite.*

Animal glue and contact adhesive are unsuitable. The former because it sets too quickly and the latter because it will not allow the laminations to 'slide' into position in the formers.

Note: If a complicated lamination is being made up, it is best to use a resin glue with a separate slow-setting hardener.

CURVED LAMINATIONS

In addition to the possibilities of curved work in furniture-designing, you will recognise the importance of the strong curved laminations in such items as skis, toboggan runners and canoe paddles. Hand laminating in the workshop is mainly in narrow material. It is possible to laminate large areas successfully, e.g. chair seats, but success can only be guaranteed with the use of a vacuum bag made of rubber or polythene.

LAMINATING EQUIPMENT FOR CURVED LAMINATION

To achieve the desired shape (or form), the laminations are secured between or around a **former**. Formers are of three main kinds:

1. **Solid wood blocks**
2. **Open wood frames**
3. **Flexible metal bands**

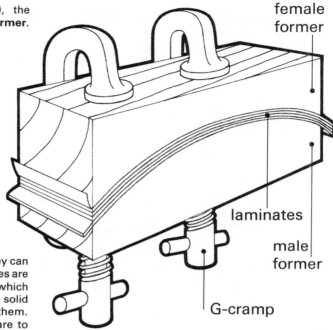

1. SOLID WOOD BLOCKS

These are used for smaller work because they can be prepared with considerable accuracy. All types are a variation of the simple example illustrated which consists of male and female formers, cut from solid wood with the laminates sandwiched between them. *Note:* Make formers out of hardwood if they are to be used frequently.

PREPARING THE FORMERS

The curves are accurately drawn on the block and are sawn to the approximate shape (preferably with a bandsaw). The curves are then accurately finished, using a circular plane or spokeshave, with allowances being made for the thickness of the laminations.

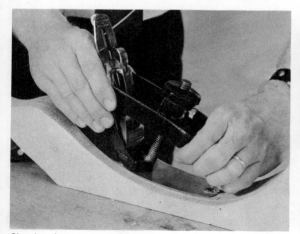

Circular plane on curved former.

PREPARING THE LAMINATIONS

These are cut from a sheet of veneer or are machine-sawn from solid material. The latter method is wasteful as up to fifty per cent of the wood is sawn away. Sawn timber must be checked for flatness and, if necessary, trued with a veneering tooth plane.

Tooth plane on saw-cut veneer.

GLUING UP

Place all the parts in position and have ready a number of G-cramps suitable for the size of the work.

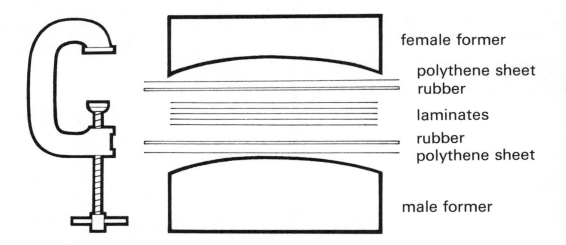

female former

polythene sheet
rubber

laminates

rubber
polythene sheet

male former

Make a trial run with the work dry and check that the pressure is adequate and even. The use of a thin rubber sheet or webbing will eliminate slight discrepancies.

Dismantle the parts, then apply the glue and cramp up as before.

Avoid glue wastage by spreading the glue with a rubber roller such as is used for lino printing.

The thin beads of surplus glue that are squeezed out should be wiped off with a damp cloth to make cleaning up easier.

The strips of polythene prevent the work from sticking to the formers or the rubber pressure pad.

Four laminated softwood arches being constructed. The last is in the jig whilst the others are being trimmed to size.

2. THE OPEN WOOD FORMER

Open wood formers are constructed where wide laminations must be done by hand, e.g. for chair seats. They are made from slabs of blockboard joined together with softwood slats which are set flush with the edges or glued and screwed onto them.

Because such shapes as stool or chair seats, made from 3 mm plywood, are relatively simple, only a male former may be needed. A means of stiffening is necessary to spread the pressure of the G-cramps over the whole surface and this is usually done with full-width cramping blocks.

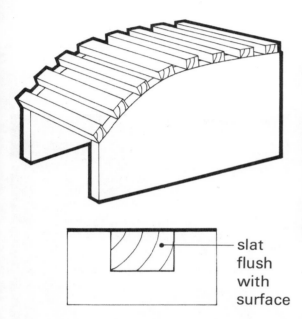

slat
flush
with
surface

3. THE FLEXIBLE METAL BAND

This is a heavy-duty, spring-steel, flexible band with a series of holes along its length. It is screwed through the holes to angle brackets which are set out on a sheet of blockboard according to the shape required.

Its chief advantages over the wooden formers are:
● the shape is quickly and accurately set out.
● complicated shapes are easily cramped up.
● the band can be re-used for any number of different shapes.

PREPARING THE BAND

The shape required is drawn full size onto a thick slab of blockboard and the surface covered with a sheet of polythene to prevent the work sticking to the board. The angle brackets are positioned so that they give support where it is most needed, i.e. near curves. The spring-steel band is screwed into place.

PREPARING THE LAMINATIONS

The laminations are cut from a sheet and selected according to the type of work being done. Select 1·5 mm thick for most types of chair bend and 2 mm for the straighter work. The laminate is too thick if it will not bend dry without showing signs of cracking.

GLUING UP

A dry trial run should be made, using a rubber pressure pad to ensure a smooth stain-free finish to the work. A second strip of rubber is sandwiched between the work and the plain steel band, which supports the laminates as they are shaped. Glue is applied with a roller and the surplus glue that is squeezed out should be wiped off with a damp cloth.

When possible, use part of a previously made bend as the partial former for the next one, ensuring an accurate fit and saving time.

THE FLEXIFORMER AND FLEXICRAMP

The 75 mm wide *Flexiformer* used on the chair frame (see page 129) can be fitted with a vice-type screw and is then called a *Flexicramp*.

Used with a plain internal steel band and angle brackets, it acts as a tensioning former for 'circuit' laminations, e.g. guitar bodies, and tray and table rims.

A cramp fitment enables the veneer bends to be adjusted to a good fit before cramping up, and for their butt joints to be closed. It also allows the perforated spring steel band to be slackened off so that the inner veneer can be removed and glue applied to the inner surface of the outer bend while it is in position. The inner bend is then replaced and a plain spring band is inserted to spread pressure from the cramps.

BENDING SOLID TIMBERS

INTRODUCTION

In spite of the popularity of making wooden bends using laminations, it is quicker and cheaper for many shapes, such as some chair and boat-building parts, to be made from solid wood, using hand-bending methods. Solid wood bends will seldom maintain the exact shape required because of changes in moisture content. If absolute accuracy is essential, then it is better to use lamination.

Bentwood chair.

When the first two bends have been glued up, one by one, the exterior may be finished by the application of a fine surface veneer with impact adhesive.

TIMBERS USED

The Windsor chair-makers of Buckinghamshire, used local-grown Ash, Elm and Yew for their constructions. The seat was of hardwearing Elm and the frame bent from Yew. Research during the past decade has shown that, although Yew bends well, the other two timbers can be bent more easily without breaking.

The list below is divided into five categories of 'bendability'.

Very Good
Ash
Beech
Birch
Elm
Hickory
Oak
Sycamore
Walnut (European)

Good
Horse-Chestnut
Mansonia
Yew

Moderate
Afrormosia
Agba
Lime
Mahogany (African)
Obeche
Rauli
Teak

Poor
Sapele
Spruce
Very Poor
Abura
Cedar, Western Red
Ramin
Seraya
Utile

BENDING EQUIPMENT

Much of the equipment required can be made in the workshop; the most important item is the steaming chest. Solid wood is more bendable when it is steamed or soaked in boiling water for a period of time—about forty-five minutes to one hour per 25 mm of thickness. Of the various 'Heath Robinson' steaming chests or tubs that have been made in the past, the best have certain common features:

The chest should be strong and steamproof, e.g. large diameter piping with an adequate seal.

It has a steam inlet—preferably near the bottom of the chest.

It has a small outlet pipe at the top of the chest.

There is a drainage hole for excess moisture—the chest can be tilted.

There is lagging to prevent heat loss—glassfibre is ideal.

Bending chest

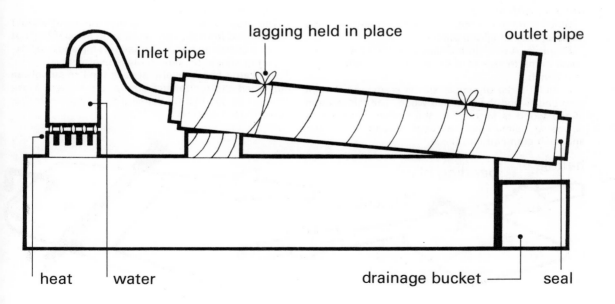

inlet pipe   lagging held in place   outlet pipe

heat   water   drainage bucket —— seal

BENDING

Once the timber has become bendable, it is taken from the chest and pulled into the position required.

Bending without straps

Large bends can be made by forcing the timber:
● around stout pegs or blocks fixed to a baseboard,
● between male and female formers,
● over a stout metal male former.

The disadvantages of the above methods are:
● bending over pegs tends to mark softwoods
● the bend takes a long time to dry out when bent between formers.

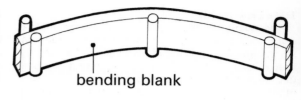

bending blank

bending over pegs

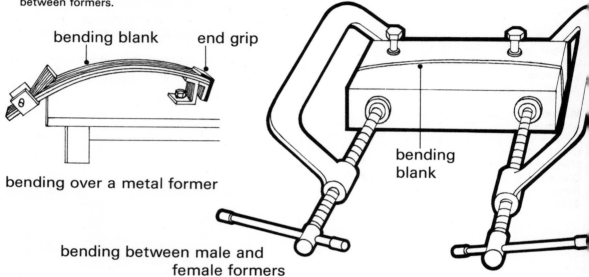

bending blank   end grip

bending over a metal former

bending blank

bending between male and female formers

Bending with straps

Small diameter bends require the support of straps made of mild or spring steel.

Example: A chair frame needs a solid wood former, equal to the thickness of the wood to be bent, bolted to a bench.

A metal strap of similar size is cramped between the handles and the steamed wood. The mid-section of the wood is secured to the former and the two halves are simultaneously bent around the former and sash cramped into place.

REMOVING THE WORK

The wood sets as it dries so that the 'bend' should be removed from the former as soon as possible (but in not less than an hour). The sash cramp and supporting strap should be kept in place overnight.

Note: Large bends nearly always tend to straighten out when the restraining cramp is removed. Make allowances for this by bending to a slightly smaller curve than is required.

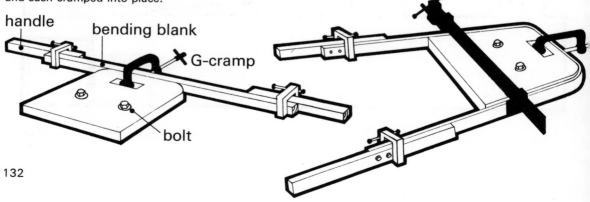

handle   bending blank

G-cramp

bolt

EXAMINATION QUESTIONS

LAMINATING

1. The drawing shows the plan and front elevation of a curved seat for a stool.

(a) Describe, step by step, the way you would make this curved seat, using freehand sketches to illustrate your answer.

(b) Show how you would hold the work for the final shaping. (MET)

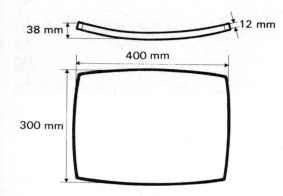

2. The drawing shows the rocker of a rocking chair which could be made either by steam bending or by laminated construction.

(a) Explain briefly both methods and use free-hand drawings to illustrate your answer.

(b) Name a wood that is suitable for steam bending. (MET)

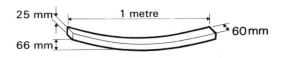

3. If a piece of Ash 200 mm by 6 mm is bent round a former to make a toast rack it will probably break. Describe briefly:

(a) how this operation can be carried out successfully.

(b) the main pieces of apparatus required.

Use drawings to illustrate your answers where possible. (MET)

4. Draw out and explain your design for a former for the chair frame above.

5. Use notes and sketches to show how you would make an open former to manufacture the plywood bins shown below.

Assuming that each bin is 250 mm high and 250 mm in diameter write out a cutting list of the material needed to make each one.

6. The sketch shows an easy chair. The curved support, 35 mm wide by 22 mm thick for the arm, is to be laminated from 3 mm thick veneers. Describe how you would form this support.

9 UPHOLSTERY

Upholstery, like wood-turning or laminating, is a craft in itself. The aim of this chapter is to give sufficient information for you to upholster your own work— perhaps a stool or low chair. Some basic tools are listed and the materials required can usually be bought in local shops.

TOOLS REQUIRED

Small screwdriver
Flexible tape
Ballpoint pen
Rubber adhesive
French chalk
Calico
Stapling gun (label tacker)
Sewing equipment

Stapler with fence set, ensuring even stapling from edge of work.

FILLER MATERIALS

The traditional materials, used since early times, such as horsehair, have largely been replaced by two basic materials:
1. **Latex foam**
2. **Polyether foam**

LATEX FOAM
This is a mixture of natural and man-made latex, combined to produce a soft, ventilated and resilient material. Apart from ready-made cushions, you can buy three types of foam:

Cavity sheet: 25—100 mm thick; smooth top-surface and varying degrees of firmness.

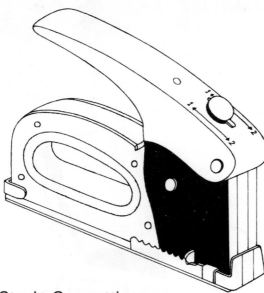

Staple Gun settings
1 Medium strike
2 Hard strike

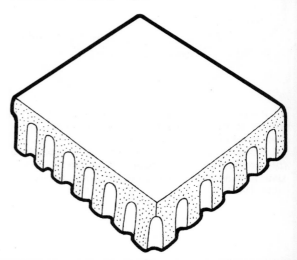

Plain sheet: 12—30 mm thick; both sides smooth.

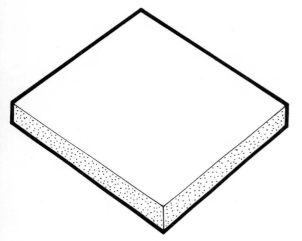

Pin-core cavitation: 25—100 mm thick; can be cut for seating without the need for side walling.

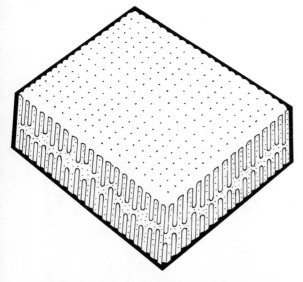

Latex foam is not cheap but will last for many years without losing its shape or firmness.

POLYETHER (PLASTIC) FOAM

This should not be confused with the light, soft polyester foam used for backing some upholstery and clothing materials. Apart from individually-moulded cushions, there are two main kinds:

Slabstock foam: produced in large blocks of varying grades which can be sliced to any thickness.

Reconstituted foam: off-cuts of slabstock foam, shredded and mixed with liquid foam which bonds them together.

As foams of different qualities are similar in texture, they are coloured according to their type. Below is a guide to the density of the foam but the hardness is best tested by touch.

DUNLO-PREME CODE	Colour	Density	Hard-ness	Use
D17	Dark/grey	Heavy	Firm	Seating (especially on webbing).
D13	Peach	Heavy	Firm	Seating (best quality)
D10	White	Medium	Medium/ Soft	Backs (best quality) & topping General padding (arms etc.)
D9	Turquoise	Medium/ hard	Medium	Seating
D8	Light grey	Medium/ hard	Medium	Backs of good quality
DR 61—65	Bonded foams various	Heavy	Firm	Solid seats & edge supports

BASE OR PLATFORM MATERIALS

There are four types of bases or platforms:
1. **Webbing**
2. **Diaphragm**
3. **Hardboard**
4. **Plywood**

WEBBING

Pirelli resilient webbing consists of two layers of rayon cords cut on the bias, bonded together, and sandwiched with rubber to form a flat 'spring'. The cords do not stretch. As the webbing is tensioned, the bias-cut, fabric layers turn towards the axis of the webbing.

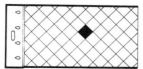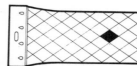

The two most common grades of webbing are:

Standard for seats beds and settees. Use 19 mm and 28 mm for backs and 38 mm, 51 mm and 57 mm for seats. Beige, brown or black.
Super 70 webbing for soft seating. Use 38 mm or 51 mm widths. Mid-brown in colour.

THE DIAPHRAGM

The *Pirelli* four-point platform is a rubber diaphragm fixed by triangular steel loops to four points—usually the legs. This throws less strain on the construction than webbing does. The top surface is smooth but the bottom shows the load-bearing construction and the thickened outside edge.

A guide to platform sizes:

Platform number	Unstretched size	Stretched dimensions	
		At 15% maximum tension	At 8% minimum tension
BX 150	380 mm²	438 mm²	413 mm²
BX 166	425 mm²	490 mm²	457 mm²
BX 184	470 mm²	540 mm²	508 mm²

Note: The platform must not be stretched more than fifteen per cent in any direction.

Right
The underside of the diaphragm showing the ribbed surface which gives strength.

The platforms are fixed to wood frames in one of two ways:
(1) The slotted screw-stud is screwed into a pre-drilled hole in the side of the seat rail or leg. An inserting tool is available to make this task easier.

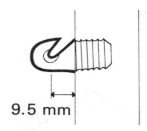

9.5 mm

(2) A mushroom-headed rivet is driven into a predrilled hole in a bevelled rail or corner block. The corner loops of the platform are engaged before the rivet is driven home. This will prevent the platform from slipping off.

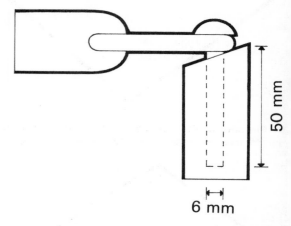

50 mm

6 mm

'FABWEB'

A platform for seats can be made using *Pirelli Fabweb*—a combination of a panel of resilient webbing securely sewn to a strong woven polyurethane fabric.

If the platform material will not stretch more than 2 cm per metre, and the recommended sewing instructions are followed (see *p. 143*), standard *Pirelli* webbing may be used to fabricate similar platforms in the workshop.

fabweb

'Fabweb' on upholstered frames

Back sew the cover fabric to the front edge of the platform. Staple the webbing through a tacking strip to the back of the frame.

Incorporate a thin layer (6—10 mm) of foam under the cover fabric; tension the seat and staple under the front edge of the frame.

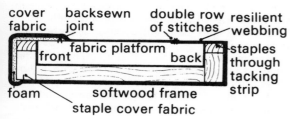

'Fabweb' on exposed wood frames

Rebate the front rail of the frame and, using a cardboard tacking strip, back staple the fabric platform into place.

Tension the seat and staple the webbing strip at the back. Alternatively groove the back rail and use steel clips (see *p. 142*).

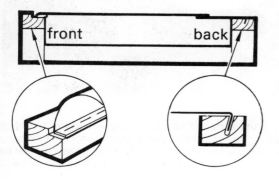

TENSIONING TOOL

It is important that the seat platform is held in tension whilst the free edge is secured.

A suitable tool (overall length to suit the width of the seat frame) can be made in the workshop from dowel (38 mm diameter), steel tube, 'beater' (32 × 12 mm) and 50 mm round nails.

The steel tube handles should be fixed with recessed 6 mm bolts and the heads of the nails, inserted at 25 mm intervals, removed to grip the fabric or webbing when stapling.

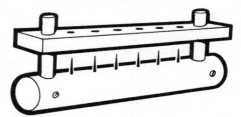

HARDBOARD

Perforated hardboard is an ideal solid base for latex and polyether foams. It allows the latex to breathe (preventing sweating) and with a built-up polyether cushion, provides a firm, comfortable seat.

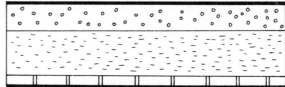

PLYWOOD

Plywood or blockboard (12 mm to 19 mm) is best used for drop-in seating. It must be drilled to allow for ventilation and, where PVC covers are used, to allow surplus air to escape.

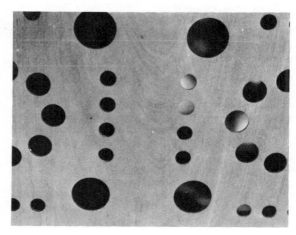

COVERS

The guide below to materials will help you to choose a suitable cover for your work.

Basic materials are:

1. **Natural fibres**
2. **Man-made fibres**
3. **PVC surfaced sheet**

Many well-known upholstery materials are a combination of two or more of these.

NATURAL FIBRES

Wool is the basis of many moquettes and is often strengthened with rayon or with expensive mohair. This blend is perfect for seats—wearing well and not causing shine on clothes. It is also woven into tweeds which are more popular than the heavier moquettes.

Cotton is an adaptable material but, although it may be made unshrinkable, fadeless, and drip-dry, it is often too light for outer covers and is used to make calico, and as a woven base for PVC sheeting.

Linen is strong and hardwearing. It washes well and is ideal for loose covers.

MAN-MADE FIBRES

These are made from chemical substances, converted into liquid form and forced through fine holes. The liquid is then solidified to form fibres which are of uniform quality throughout. There are over a thousand fibre names in use—those listed below are used in upholstery covers.

Acrylic: *Acrilan, Courtelle, Orlon.* There are many variations using mixtures of Acrylic and rayon fibres such as *Courtelle/Evlan.*

Nylon: *Bri-nylon, Celon, Enkalon.*

Using stretch yarns, nylon is suitable for cushions and close-fitting chair covers. It is washable, tough, non-shrinkable, resists abrasion, is colour-fast and is made in an innumerable variety of attractive prints.

Rayon: *Courtaulds Rayon, Fibro* and modified rayon, e.g. *Evlan.*

Rayon is a versatile material normally mixed with cotton or wool to give it strength and to produce different colour/texture effects. *Evlan,* which was developed for use in carpet manufacture, has wearing properties ideal for upholstery seating.

PVC SURFACED SHEET

Vinyl-coated cotton fabric has become a common feature of modern upholstery. It is easy to stitch; it can be made in an unlimited range of prints, and many different effects, such as the 'leather look' can be produced. Brand names include—*Vynide, Everflex, Storoflex.*

The unsupported vinyl sheets, such as *Novon, Storvic, Vyweld* are thin grades without backing.

They have a tendency to puncture and tear unless firmly padded but they can be used for kitchen-stool seats and for padded headboards.

Knitted base fabrics are sometimes called jersey-backed, e.g. *Flexnit, Ambla, Cirrus.* Further developments have produced 'a soft, supple material with an expanded PVC layer sandwiched between the skin and the backing.

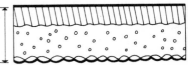

Knitted base fabrics possess high stretch qualities, are durable, soil-resistant and easy to stitch, tack or staple.

BUYING MATERIAL

Buy the best you can afford.

Use only materials designed for upholstery—some weaves are too light.

Ask to see material in natural light—artificial light alters colours considerably.

CARE OF MATERIALS

When buying **natural-fibre material**, ask if there are specific washing or cleaning instructions from the manufacturers. If so, follow them carefully.

Woven fabrics can generally be vacuumed to remove dust, and stains can be removed with a cleaning agent applied sparingly with a soft cloth. Some fluids attack latex foam, and covers must be removed to be cleaned.

Man-made fibres are often treated with stain repellant, e.g. *Scotchgard.* If not, as with natural fibres, they can be sprayed with silicone liquid.

This treatment makes fabrics waterproof and practically impervious to stains. Normal household stains, marks, or spilt liquids can easily be wiped away without being absorbed.

PVC surfaced sheet is easily cleaned with soap or mild detergent and a damp cloth, followed by rinsing in clean water and drying. Abrasive powders must be avoided and polish may even damage the surface.

UPHOLSTERY MATERIALS IN USE

The following examples show some ways in which upholstery materials could be used in the workshop.

LOUNGE STOOL 1
Dark **hardwood frame** and **white cover**.
    Platform—plywood or blockboard
    Filling—latex cavity foam or dense plastic foam
    Cover—jersey-backed, expanded PVC

1. MAKING THE PLATFORM
The blockboard is cut to size. Ventilation holes are drilled and sharp edges are removed.

2. THE FILLING
Most types of foam can be marked out with a ball-point pen and cut with sharp, large-bladed scissors or a long knife. Plastic foam will cut easily on a band-saw. All types of foam suffer from loss of thickness in use and to prevent seats from 'hollowing', the foam must be cut oversize. A guide is three per cent in both length and width and ten per cent in thickness. For seating use only high density foams which lose less thickness.

3. FIXING THE FILLING
Use self-adhesive tape or 50 mm wide calico strip glued to the foam to secure it to the base. Dust with French chalk or talcum powder.
Note: For this and subsequent fixings, a stapler, which can be used one-handed, is preferable to the traditional use of tacks.

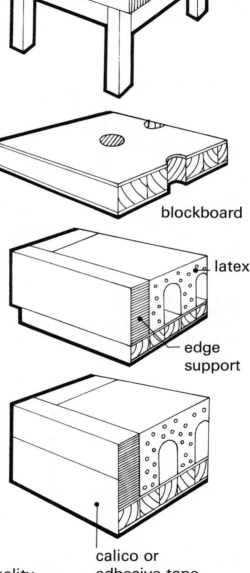

blockboard

latex

edge support

calico or adhesive tape

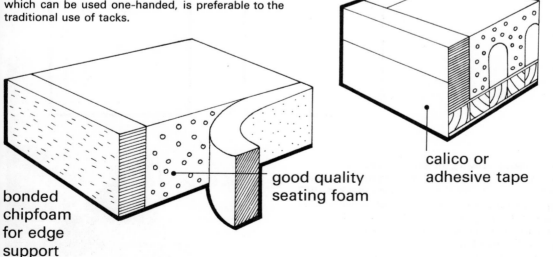

bonded chipfoam for edge support

good quality seating foam

4. THE COVER

The cover should be cut to size with a 50 mm turn under allowed at each edge.

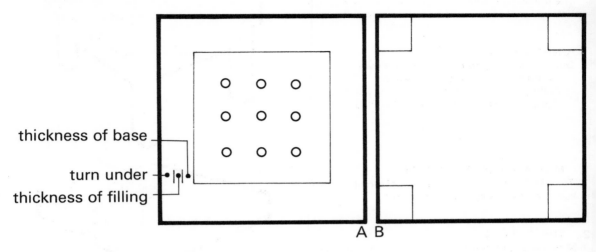

thickness of base

turn under

thickness of filling

A B

Lay the base on the reverse of the cover and mark the corners of the base. (A)

Draw lines from these points at right angles to the edge of the cover. (B)

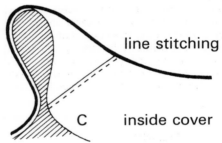

line stitching

inside cover

Fold the material so that the lines meet. Pin into place and sew up. (C)

Use temporary tacks or staples in the centre of each side to position the cover on the base. (D)

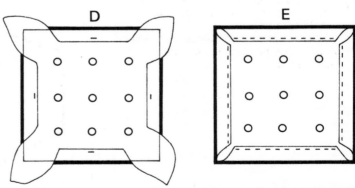

D

E

Fix the sides, leaving the corners free. (E)

The corner fold presents a problem of surplus material. You will find that the woven-backed PVC cuts easily with scissors and its stretch quality makes it simple to fit. Practise first with an off-cut to decide which part of the inner fold to cut away. Treat all corners in the same way.

Use a knife and a straight edge to trim the material.

140

LOUNGE STOOL 2

Made in **Oak**, inlaid with **Walnut**, with a **coloured cover**.

    Platform—plywood
    Filling—cavity latex foam with plain sheet
    Cover—PVC coated cotton fabric

LOUNGE STOOL 3

Made in **Teak** with a richly-woven, **tweed-covered, loose cushion**.

    Platform—*Pirelli* diaphragm
    Filling—High density, medium-hard plastic foam.
    Cover—tweed fabric.

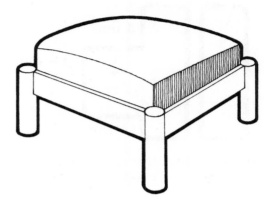

MAKING THE SEAT

Follow the instructions as for **Lounge Stool 1**, but remember the following special features:

Holes are bored in the platform to allow for ventilation and the filling should be 'feathered' to produce a round edge.

SPECIAL FEATURES

A calico cover must be used between the filling and the woven tweed. The loose cushion is reversible and is made with a nylon zipper or a *Velcro* fastening for easy removal for cleaning.

No ventilation panels are needed because the material weave is open-textured.

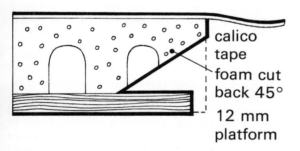

calico
tape
foam cut
back 45°
12 mm
platform

A domed effect is achieved by gluing a piece of plain sheet to the underside of the cavity sheet.

ALTERNATIVE PLATFORM—WEBBING

If the side rails of the stool are strong enough, *Pirelli* webbing can be taken round them and secured on the inside with tacks or long staples.

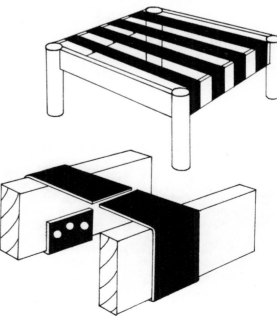

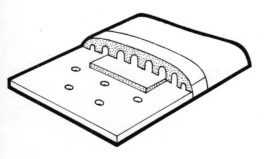

It is usual, however, for the webbing to be held by steel clips, slotted into grooves cut into the top edge of the stool rails. The grooves can be cut at an angle of about 10° to 15° on a circular saw.

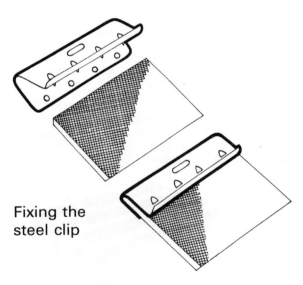

chair frame bed frame-the fillet gives extra strength

Fixing the steel clip

Fixing webbing clip in vice.

Below is a table of recommended overall lengths, including overlap beyond tacks or inside clips, for 50 mm wide webbing and 'medium' seating.

For 'hard' seating subtract 12 mm from each length and for 'soft' seating add 12 mm.

SEAT SPAN	STANDARD	SUPER 70
460 mm	435 mm	410 mm
510 mm	485 mm	445 mm
560 mm	522 mm	485 mm
610 mm	572 mm	535 mm

ADHESIVES SUITABLE FOR DIFFERENT MATERIALS

Foams and PVC covers react adversely to some adhesives. Select an adhesive specially made for a particular job. The chart below will help you. Always read the manufacturer's instructions carefully.

To bond:

PVC sheet to plastic foam	Evo-stik 5007/3	or Clam 7
Plastic foam to wood	Evo-stik 5007/3	or Clam 58
PVC sheet to wood	Evo-stik 5007/3	or Clam 58
PVC sheet to metal	Evo-stik 8383	or Clam 2
Leather to metal	Evo-stik 528	or Clam 3
Rubber to rubber	Evo-stik 524	or Dunlop rubber solution

'VELCRO' FASTENERS

The Velcro fastener is made from two nylon strips, one with thousands of small hooks and the other with thousands of small loops. When the strips are pressed together they produce a secure fastening and yet they can be separated by peeling them apart. Velcro can be stitched or glued to almost any material and cut to length with scissors.

In upholstery, it is used for cushion fastenings (where the cover has to be removable for cleaning) and for hidden joints, where stitching is difficult.

'A touch and it is closed'

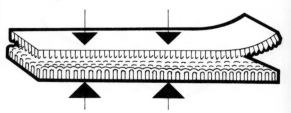

SEWING

The secret of success in sewing upholstery lies in choosing the right materials for the job.

The combinations shown below of thread size, needle size and number of stitches per 25 mm, are from the 'English Sewing' range and used correctly will produce satisfactory results.

Fabrics	Thread	Needle	Stitches per 25 mm
Calico	Dewhurst Star	Round point 18–19	10
Tweeds	Dewhurst Strongthread	Round point 18–19	10
Woven-back PVC	Dewhurst Strongthread	Round point 19–21	8
Stretch Nylon	Dewhurst Star	Ball point 14–16	12
Fabweb	Dewhurst Strongthread	Round point 19–21	8

EXAMINATION QUESTIONS

UPHOLSTERY

1. You have to choose a filler for:
(a) a child's mattress
(b) a seat for an elderly woman
   Write down all the considerations you should take into account when making your choice.

2. What kind of cover would you use for the following jobs? Give your reasons.
(a) a kitchen-stool top
(b) a lounge chair
(c) a padded headboard for a bed

3. Use notes and sketches to describe what is meant by:
(a) bonded chipfoam
(b) a rubber diaphragm
(c) plain sheet latex

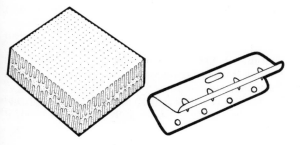

4. Write what you know about the two items drawn below.

5. Make a series of sketches to show two ways of fixing resilient webbing to the rails of a stool.

6. A complete seat and back support for a chair is to be made from *Pirelli Fabweb* as shown.
   Make detailed notes and drawings to show how the material would be fixed to a framework at points A, B, and C.

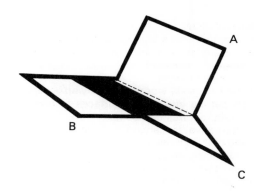

7. *(a)* *Pirelli* resilient webbing is often used as a base for upholstered seats, name *two* other types of bases. *(b)* By means of sketches show *two* ways of fixing resilient webbing to the rails of a stool. *(c)* By means of sketches show what size of covering would be required for a seat which has a base 450 mm × 300 mm × 20 mm and a 30 mm thick latex foam filling. *(d)* Explain how a 'velcro' fastener works.

10 WOODCARVING AND SCULPTURE

INTRODUCTION

This chapter gives a brief guide to suitable carving timbers, a survey of holding and cutting tools, and some suggested pieces of work on which to base your own designs and ideas.

Carving from solid wood is a satisfying occupation, although cutting into timber surfaces to reveal unknown grain features can be hard work.

An alternative to carving is to collect pieces of wood and make shapes to assemble together to form a three-dimensional piece of sculpture. The making of built-up assemblies offers scope for the imagination and generally requires less time.

Carved sculpture is often based on the human figure or on animal forms, whilst assemblies are frequently abstract forms.

SUITABLE CARVING TIMBERS

The following timbers are best suited to surface carving and detailed work:

Beech   A hard, pinkish-coloured wood. The straight, uninteresting grain is difficult to work but finishes smoothly.
Use: tableware, spoons etc.

Boxwood   A hard, close-grained wood which cuts cleanly. Its creamy yellow appearance is familiar on chisel handles.
Use: detailed carving, e.g. Chessmen.

Ebony   A very hard wood which is only available in small sizes. Traditionally used for the black notes of pianos and chessmen, it cuts cleanly and takes a smooth finish.
Use: detailed work.

Jarrah   A hard, close-grained, heavy wood similar in colour to mahogany. It cuts cleanly and is extremely durable.
Use: nameplates.

Lignum Vitae   The hardest of woods, usually dark green in colour with brown streaks. It is ideal for detailed work and takes a high polish.
Use: small figures and touch shapes.

Lime   A close-grained, creamy-yellow wood which cuts easily. Available in large sizes and for most jobs. It is considered the best carvers' material.
Use: decorative work of all kinds.

Mahogany   The different types vary in hardness and colour. The most suitable for carving are hard, close-grained, deep red woods which take a good finish.
Use: panels, figures etc.

Rosewood   This reddish-purple wood with darker streaks is hard and polishes well. Mainly cut into small sizes, it is used for quality, detailed work.
Use: paperknives and touch shapes.

Sycamore   A hard creamy-white wood which takes a good finish.
Use: tableware of all kinds.

The second group of timbers below are more suitable for three dimensional work.

Cherry   A hard wood with an even texture. It is pinkish in colour with attractive markings.

Elm   Its hard, attractive wild grain comes in various shades of brown and, although often difficult to carve, the large sizes are ideal for major works.

Oak   It is similar to elm in many ways. Its open grain needs bold treatment and finish.

Pear   A hard, pink-yellow wood which, like most fruit woods, can be used for detailed work.

Pines   These vary in hardness and in colour from white to red. Their attractive grains need sharp tools to obtain a good finish. They are available in large sizes and are relatively cheap.

Teak   A hard, rich brown, oily wood with an even grain. It carves well but quickly blunts cutting edges. It is extremely durable and is consequently an ideal material for outdoor jobs.

Walnut   A hard, brown wood which is often well figured. It takes a good polish and is suitable for figure work and touch shapes.

Yew   This is a hard, pinkish softwood with an attractive grain. It is durable, polishes well and is ideal for work of all sizes.

TOOLS—HOLDING DEVICES

The variety in size and shape of carved work tests the sculptor's ingenuity to keep his work secure. For most jobs, holding devices in general workshop use are adequate. They are:

- **a bench vice**
- **a G-cramp**
- **a holdfast**
- **handscrews**

Special holding devices include the following:

THE CARVER'S CHOPS

This vice is held by a bolt passed through the bench and tightened by a wing nut. The padded jaws prevent work from being damaged.

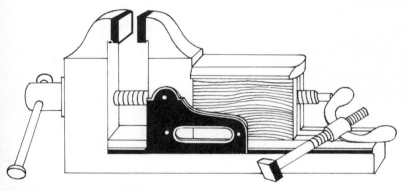

THE CARVER'S BENCH SCREW

This screw can be used to secure work to the bench. Like the carver's chops, it is easily rotated, making sculpture from the solid less difficult.

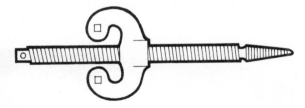

THE CLIP OR BUTTON

Panels to be carved in low relief are held in place by pairs of metal clips screwed to the bench top.

Bench screw in use.

THE RACK CRAMP

The deep-throat version of the fully adjustable rack cramp will hold most wide work. The iron rack enables great pressure to be applied but a lighter aluminium version is also available.

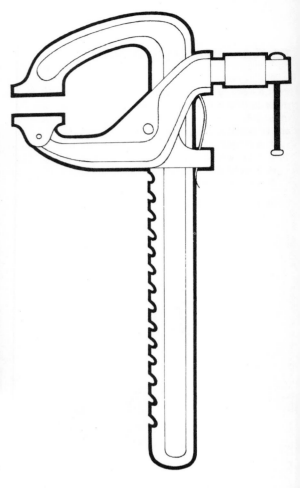

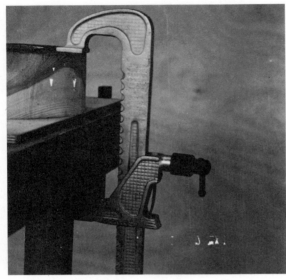

Aluminium cramp in use.

CUTTING TOOLS

Panels and low relief carving are done from prepared boards.

Large, three-dimensional work is often done from the log. Before use, the wood must be carefully dried out.

Note: Splitting—a common fault—is less likely to occur if the carving is spread over a period of time.

THE LOG SAW

This is used for cutting blocks roughly to size.

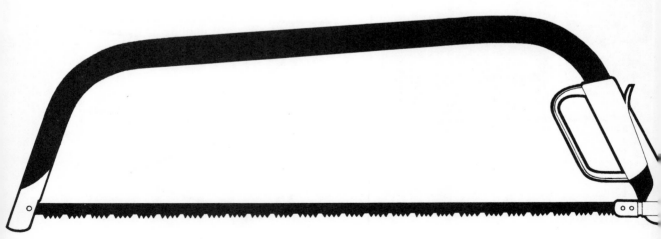

OTHER SAWS

Bandsaws and jig saws are able to remove bulk waste quickly, and bowsaws do similar work if machinery is not available. Waste on thinner wood may be removed with a coping saw.

THE AXE AND ADZE

These are two useful edge tools also for removing large areas of waste material in a short time. Great care must be taken not to split the grain with them.

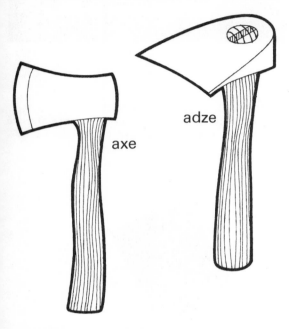

axe

adze

THE CARVING MALLET

This is made from Beech or Lignum Vitae with an Ash handle. Mallets vary in size and therefore weight, and are used according to the type of work being done.

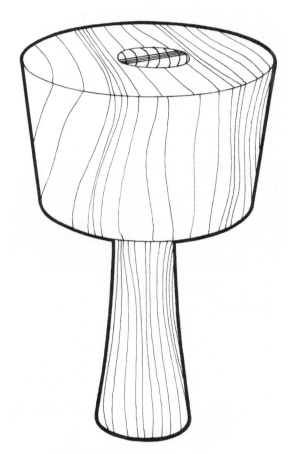

CHISELS AND GOUGES

Large sculptures often consist of simple curves that can be cut with chisels and standard scribing, or firmer gouges (see *Woodwork 1, p. 109*). For almost every conceivable shape, however, a gouge has been invented. Gouges are given names such as bent, back bent, fluters, veiners, spade, parting and fishtail. They are made in a variety of sizes up to 25 mm wide, although most work can be done with straight gouges of varying widths and sections.

Gouges are classified in three ways:
    The shape of the blade, e.g. bent
    The width of the blade, e.g. 12 mm
    The blade section, e.g. No. 9
The sections illustrated are available in 12 mm widths.

OTHER CUTTING TOOLS

Bench chisels for removing waste
Spokeshaves for finishing curves
Large **twist bits** for boring holes.

OTHER SHAPING AND FINISHING TOOLS

RASPS AND FILES

Rasps and files can be used on wood to remove gouge marks prior to glass-papering to a smooth finish. Awkward corners are reached using **rifflers**—small files of various shapes and sections.

The **Rawflex 'file'** is a canvas mitt which is partly covered with narrow strips of carbon steel. The abrasive quality of the material makes it possible to use it not only on wood but also on plastic laminate, fibreglass and soft metals. Convex curves may be shaped with a Rawflex file wrapped round the hand.
Note: If rasps and files clog, clean with a wire brush.

The Rawlflex mitt is made from canvas with strips of abrasive barbed steel glued to part of the surface.

THE SURFORM RANGE

The non-clog Surform range perform a similar function to rasps and files. Some sculptors are inclined to use these tools in preference to the more orthodox gouges. (See *Woodwork 1, pp. 63—64.*)

The ripping plane shown is the latest addition to the *Surform* range. The teeth of the curved blade face the handle and the plane is pulled towards the user.

THE PORTABLE POWER UNIT AND THE LATHE

These can be used in sculpture by fitting a flexible drive shaft, e.g. *Leindrive*, to drive items such as the **Surform drum cutter**, small diameter **drum sanders** or **rotary files** for detailed work.

TEMPERED STEEL SCRAPERS

These may be used for smooth surfaces and are ground to fit into the curve being scraped.

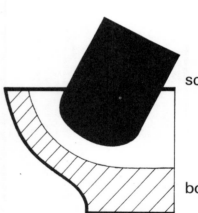

scraper

bowl section

BOWL CARVING

Round bowls, turned on the lathe, suggest the perfection and precision of the machine technique used. By forming a bowl using hand tools, you can also create shapes that are lovely to look at and to hold.

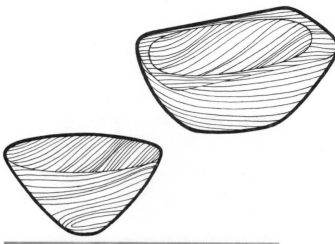

THE DESIGN

Spend some time making sketches of what the bowl will look like. In this way you are less likely to make errors when cutting out the shape. The drawings should be large and a soft pencil, crayon, or fibre pen should be used to achieve a shape, avoiding unnecessary decoration. The shape and grain are usually sufficient to make the bowl look attractive.

Draw a series of plans, side views and sections, based on the size and characteristics of the timber available.

Note: If a handle is necessary, it should be part of the design and not be 'stuck on' at a later date.

DRAWING OUT

Having decided on the shape, make a full-size pattern or template. The shape is then transferred to the surface of the wood and positioned in such a way as to avoid any faults in the wood and to take advantage of its grain markings.

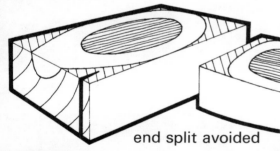

end split avoided

HOLLOWING OUT

If the shape leaves very little waste wood, the block is held in a vice, but generally G-cramps can be used to hold the wood firmly on the bench. The bulk of the waste is removed with a straight firmer gouge and mallet. If the section of the bowl side is particularly steep, a bent gouge must be used. The gouge is used from the outside of the bowl towards the centre, first working along the grain, then across it.

SURFACE TREATMENT INSIDE

The surface treatment is considered only when the shape is exactly right—free from unwanted ridges or hollows. The surface may be finished directly from a sharp gouge or scraped and glass-papered to a fine, smooth finish. Much depends on the type of wood being used.

SHAPING THE OUTSIDE

The basic outside shape is cut with a bowsaw or on a bandsaw. The bowl is then held with a bench holdfast or deep-throat cramp and the bulk of waste removed with scribing gouge. The cuts are made from the clearly-marked base outline towards the outside of the block. A large chiselling board protects the bench surface. The final shaping is done with a flat-faced spokeshave, scraper and glass-paper.

Note: The bowl may be held in a vice for working the final finish.

THE FINISH

The finish depends upon the material used and the job it has to do. The use of heat and water-resistant plastic coating for a gloss finish, and teak oil for a matt finish on hard woods is recommended.

SHALLOW DISHES

It is more convenient to shape the outside of shallow work first. A block of wood glued to the surface enables the work to be held in the vice for both shaping the outside and hollowing out. The sequence of photographs shows the various stages of the work involved.

Shape is marked from a paper template.

Block is glued to base with a paper insert.

The outside shape is cut with a bow-saw . . .

. . . and smoothed with a flat-faced spokeshave . . .

. . . or a Surform tool

A gouge is used to hollow out the bowl.

Finer cuts are made with a flatter gouge using hand pressure only.

The surface is scraped flat . . .

and smoothed with glasspaper.

The block on the under side is removed . . .

. . . and the surface cleaned off.

One attractive finish for pine is to burn the surface with the brazing torch.

The surface is then brushed with a wire brush and a suitable finish applied.

LAYERED BOWLS

To obtain a good finish boards of different timbers should be of contrasting colours but similar in texture, e.g. Sycamore and Walnut.

Plan the type and thickness of the layers carefully. Some layers may be of veneer. The layers should be glued with a PVA adhesive that will not blunt the cutting tools.

SMALL SCULPTURE
FROM THE SOLID

THE WOOD

Blocks of wood, small enough to be held in the hand, can be found in every 'short end' or 'waste-wood' box.

These are ideal for making into **touch shapes**—hand-size abstract carvings, smoothly finished and a pleasure to hold.

THE DESIGN

Worn pebbles from a beach or river bed occasionally inspire touch shapes but the material may also govern the final form of the shape.

Example: A hard knot may protrude from the basic shape and contrast with a hollow, carved to follow strong grain.

SHAPING AND FINISHING

Waste can be removed with a normal woodworking chisel and shaping done with rasps and files.

Use different grades of glass-paper to produce a smooth surface.

Touch and animal shapes should be given a smooth, hard finish, e.g. of polyurethane or plastic coating.

Note: Use a variety of woods to fashion these hand sculptures because each will tell you much about the nature of the material—valuable experience for when larger work is tackled.

Touch shapes made by young boys.

CARVING A SMALL FIGURE

When you feel confident to make a larger carving an animal figure makes a good subject.

You may be fortunate to visit a zoo or safari park to make original sketches. If not, find as many photographs of an animal as you can to study its shape—then sketch a simplified form.

The method used to make this buffalo carving is illustrated overleaf.

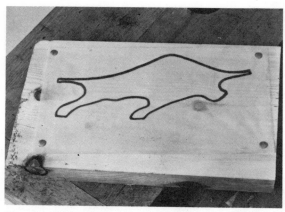

The simplified outline is transferred to the surface of the wood.

The waste-wood is removed with a frame saw.

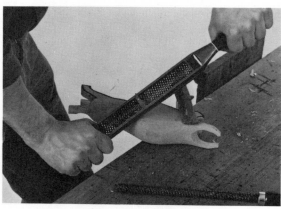

A *Surform* tool is used to round the edges . . .

. . . and a round file to clean out the corners.

Wrap glasspaper round the dowel rod to smooth concave surfaces . . .

. . . and finish with an appropriate stain and/or polish.

LARGE SCULPTURE FROM THE SOLID

When a large sculpture is planned it is necessary to find either a suitable piece of timber for the work you have designed, or to design a piece of sculpture to suit the wood available. Remember that wood can be built up to the required shape and size.

THE DESIGN

To avoid costly errors and carving shapes that look wrong, it is advisable to spend a good deal of time making sketches. Working models of clay, plasticine or plaster of Paris are also helpful. One of the world's greatest sculptors, Henry Moore, has always worked in this way, recording his ideas on paper and making models from stone, wood, clay and plaster. Henry Moore has studied natural shapes—the bone sketches are an example—and the qualities that he perceives in these objects can often be seen in his large reclining figures.

The qualities that we look for in small touch forms also appear on a much larger scale. Two or more such forms can be related to each other on a suitable base.

SHAPING THE WOOD

Bulk waste is removed with saws, axes and large gouges and shaping is done with gouges, rasps and files.

Portable power units with appropriate fittings can be used to supplement hand work, particularly in the finishing process.

The final surface treatment on large work is often varied within the same sculpture.
Example: Notice the smooth round surfaces contrasting with the gouged surfaces used to emphasize the shape of the openings in Henry Moore's *1939 Reclining Figure*.

THE FINISH

This depends upon where the sculpture is to be situated. Firstly, any major splits in the work should be filled with wedges of the same timber. Narrower cracks can be filled with a waterproof stopping of the appropriate colour or a mixture of sawdust and resin glue. Ideally, the protective coating should be clear and so emphasize the natural pattern of the grain, yet withstand weathering and/or the constant touch of inquisitive hands.

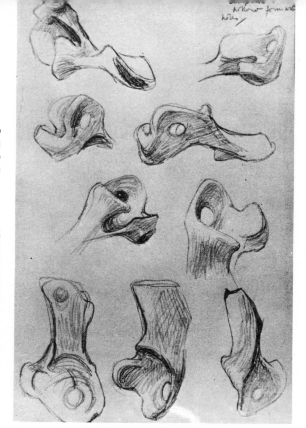

Studies of bones by Henry Moore, 1932.

'Two Forms 1934' by Henry Moore.

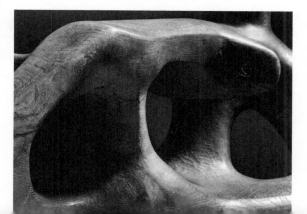

Detail from 'Reclining Figure' 1939.

BUILT-UP SCULPTURE

An assembly of several pieces of material of varying shapes, sizes, colour and texture provides a number of exciting possibilities. This type of construction was practised in the basic course for students at the Bauhaus school of architecture in Germany, during the period 1919–33.

The students of a teacher, Laszlo Moholy-Nagy, experimented with wood, metals and plastics to make built-up sculpture of beautiful proportions and perfect balance—features that later showed up in their designs of buildings, furniture and typography.

MATERIALS

Many different pieces of wood will be found in the 'waste' box and may only require a minimum amount of work on them before they can be used.

The skill in assembling pieces of wood in such a way that they look good together is different from that of the carver. The assembly system is flexible, in that pieces can be tried in position, moved about, accepted or discarded, whereas the sculptor must be able to see his finished work in advance to achieve the 'right' balance and effect.

THE DESIGN

Perhaps the best assemblies depend upon the relation of solids and spaces to each other and on simplicity of material and finish. You must discover the possibilities of the materials by your own work, but some of the simple suggestions below may be a starting point. They are abstract forms based on simple geometrical shapes and compared with carved work may be called **Hard-edge Sculpture**.

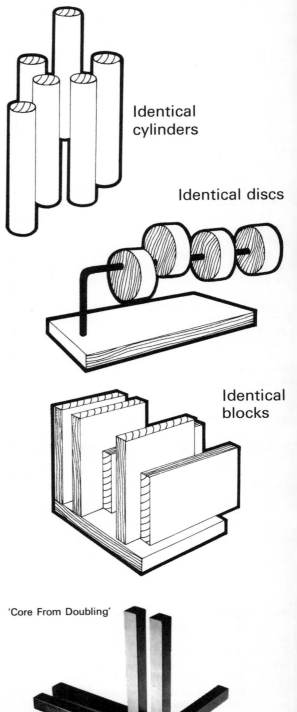

Identical cylinders

Identical discs

Identical blocks

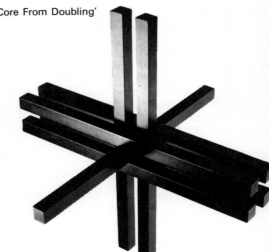

'Core From Doubling'

1 BLOCKS OF THE SAME SHAPE AND SIZE

Each of the examples shown opposite are made up of identical shapes. The interest, therefore, must come from:
- the space left between each block
- the surface finish

A classic solution to this problem is the wood-sculpture called '*Core from Doubling, 1958*' made by Max Bill, a former student at the Bauhaus.

2 BLOCKS OF THE SAME SHAPE BUT DIFFERENT SIZE

In the examples shown below, the different sizes give variety to the assembly.

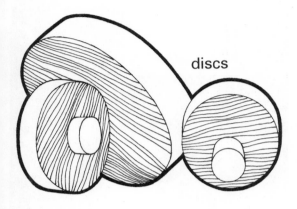

discs

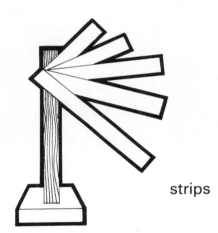

strips

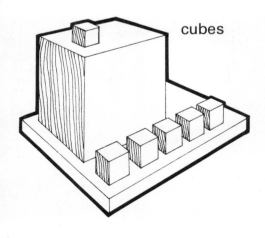

cubes

THE FINISH

Texture and colour will be provided by the wood grain, stains and paints.

A heavy texture on open-grained timbers, e.g. Pine, can be made by rubbing vigorously along the grain with a wire brush. It provides a real contrast to smooth, polished hardwood or painted surfaces.

Work to be painted can be built up from any type of 'waste wood'.

The weather-resistant properties of modern paints make the work suitable for siting outdoors.

THE DEVELOPMENT OF IDEAS

In the same way that coloured bricks are built up by young children, you may have made up a piece of sculpture that could be used as an abstract toy for a child. He may find it every bit as interesting as a wood engine—the shapes and colour may be similar but they are arranged in a different way.

Your small assembly construction could form the basis of work leading to the production of some garden play shapes for young children. They can either be small enough for the children to pick up and assemble in any way they wish—making their own sculpture, or they can be large, fixed assemblies that can be climbed on, crawled through and jumped off. *Note:* Materials for any outdoor work must be weather-resistant and have a suitable finish.

RELIEF SCULPTURE, USING CONTRASTING MATERIALS

Wood can be contrasted with other materials. Plastics and metal are ideal because they can be:
- polished to reflect light
- textured by grinding or etching
- bent or folded to a variety of shapes.

Note: Aluminium baking foil is a cheap reflective surface. It can be glued to surfaces or folded into quite complicated shapes.

Use a metal file for shaping sheet metal and a tungsten carbide-coated file (Cintride) for other hard materials, e.g. plastic, asbestos, glass etc.

The most successful contrast reliefs are those that are simple and rely on shape, surface texture and colour for effect; those that have a simple pattern theme repeated in a restricted range of materials.

The large floor sculpture by Michael Bolus (below) is made from four painted steel sections but you could use any sheet material to make-up raised surfaces. Glue two thin sheets together to make shapes permanent.

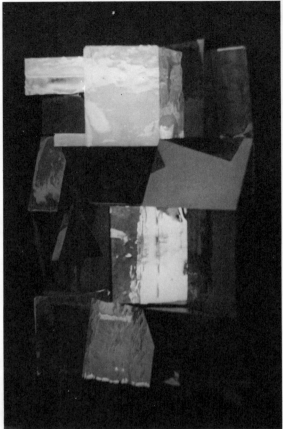

Wall sculpture in high relief—wood and aluminium:

Plywood sculpture

PRESENTATION OF WORK

Work is often spoiled by poor mounting or display. Some work will look best if it is free-standing on a surface.

Relief assemblies may be framed in simple box frames or may look best against a simple flat slab given an appropriate surface finish.

Above: Painted Unit Relief by Matt Rugg.

Below: Split limewood cylinders on a plywood base by Sergio de Camargo.

The photograph below shows work with a vertical emphasis, raised on a pillar or rod and supported on a firm base of wood or contrasting stone.

Softwood sculpture made with Surform tools by Michael Smith.

For a shallow carving a low table with a lift-off glass top and a platform screwed to the bottom edge of the enclosing side rails is an unusual but effective means of display.

The work can be changed periodically to create a point of interest in the room and the plywood platform is easily removed for its surface colour and/or texture to be altered.

EXAMINATION QUESTIONS

WOODCARVING AND SCULPTURE

1. A piece of even-grained and easily worked hardwood 350 mm by 200 mm is to be made into a shallow dish.
(a) Draw freehand a suitable shape for the dish.
(b) Draw a cross-section through the centre of the dish. (MET)

2. You have designed and carved a nut dish out of 32 mm thick material. Give in note form, together with illustrations, the sequence of operations you have worked through to produce the completed dish. Name and sketch in detail the gouge you would use.

3. Design a laminated carved dish which must not be turned on the lathe but should show an appreciation of restrained curves and flowing lines. You are expected to match woods of contrasting colour but with similar textures and suggest a suitable surface finish.

4. You wish to carve two identical shallow dishes in the shape of a leaf. At a later date you may require to carve another dish so as to complete a set of three. Explain how one can check that the set of bowls are identical bearing in mind that the original dishes will not be available when you make the third dish.

5. Describe, using notes and sketches, how you would make a flat spatula from a piece of wood measuring 200 mm × 50 mm × 6 mm. Name the tools you would require and show how you would mark out the shape, cut it and finish the edges. Name a suitable wood for the spatula.

6. Describe with the aid of sketches, the stages in carving a small figure or an abstract shape in wood. Explain how the work is held during the various stages. (MET)

7. Detail the stages in carving an animal from a solid block of wood of the measurements shown in the diagram below. What provision should be made for holding the wood while carving it?

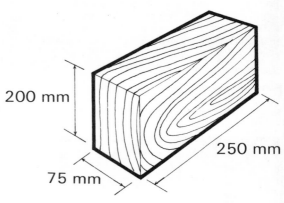

200 mm

250 mm

75 mm

8. A three dimensional, free standing woodcarving of a 'bird in flight' is required to stand on a desk or table top for display purposes. The carving when mounted on a stand must not exceed 350 mm in height and be less than 300 mm high.
Consider (a) the outline shape to give the feeling of movement in flight, (b) the influence of the grain direction, (c) the methods of carving and the influence of the tools used, (d) the surface treatment—smooth or textured, (e) method of mounting on a stand, (f) design of stand to be in keeping with the carving, (g) the surface finish. (MET)

HARDWARE

This chapter describes a selection of hardware fittings which are commonly used in cabinet and joinery work. For most examples an alternative fitting or design is available.

Steel, brass, plastic and nylon are the most usual materials for fittings. Finishes include bright steel, black japan, chromium plate, copper or bronze surfaces. Nylon is being increasingly used for many types of fitting and expensive stainless steel is generally only used when other materials are unsuitable.

DOOR FITTINGS

HINGES

These can be made from steel, nylon, or brass.

Steel hinges are used on large doors and particularly for joinery work. When fitted, half the knuckle of the steel hinge protrudes from the work.

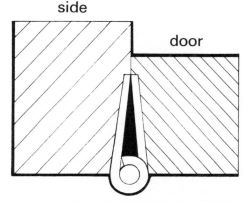

Uncranked butt hinge recessed to half the diameter of the knuckle

Nylon hinges will not rust, do not need lubricating and are ideal for large doors and for outside use. They are injection-moulded to produce tapered leaves which give added strength. Stainless steel screws should be used for fixing these hinges outdoors.

Brass hinges may be of folded metal or solid drawn. Solid-drawn hinges are stronger but more expensive and are, therefore, used only for the best work such as hardwood cabinets etc.

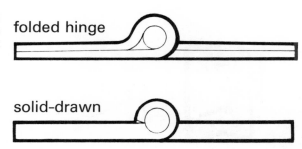

folded hinge

solid-drawn

THE BUTT HINGE

This is the most common door hinge and is made in sizes of 25—150 mm long and 25—75 mm open widths. A variation of the butt hinge is the **lift-off hinge**, which allows doors to be removed easily.

(For fitting butt hinges, see p. 173.)

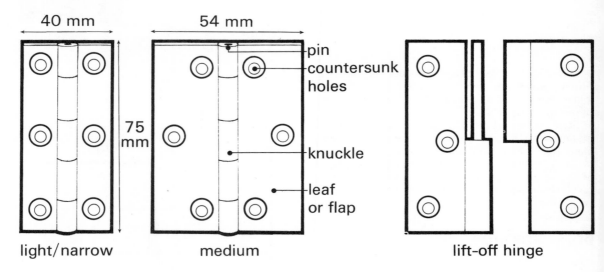

40 mm   54 mm

pin
countersunk holes
75 mm
knuckle
leaf or flap

light/narrow   medium   lift-off hinge

THE FLUSH HINGE (HURLINGE)

Unlike butt hinges, the flush hinge need not be sunk into the door edge or frame in order to look neat. The thin flaps, countersunk on opposite sides, fold one inside the other. Flush hinges are often used on softwood cabinets, e.g. for kitchen cupboard doors.
Size guide: 38—100 mm.

THE SURFACE HINGE

The surface hinge is applied to the surface of the door and cabinet.

The single cranked hinge shown is designed for use on inset doors showing only the knuckle when the door is closed. The hinge allows the door to be open through 180° and is made with a brass or chrome finish suitable for use where steam accumulates.
Size guide: 51 mm long with a 'crank' or 'set' of 16 mm.

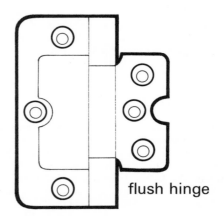

flush hinge

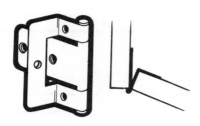

The flush hinge used on a softwood tool box.

CATCHES

The four fittings shown will hold cabinet doors in place but will not lock them.

THE BALL CATCH

The spring-loaded ball catch is fitted into a pre-drilled hole in the door stile. The flush-fitted catch plate covers a shallow hole drilled to accommodate the ball.

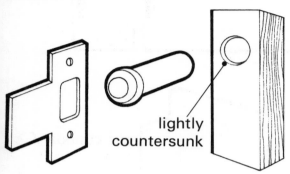

lightly
countersunk

THE CUPBOARD CATCH

This nylon catch is an alternative to the ball catch. It is quiet in use, hard-wearing and does not need oiling.

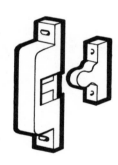

THE MAGNETIC CATCH

The magnets of this catch exert a pull of about 2 kg. The striking plate is fixed to the door and the magnet, held in a plastic case, is screwed to the carcase.

The magnetic catch is often positioned under the carcase top where it is not normally visible.

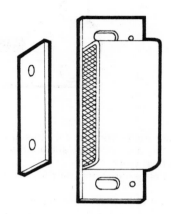

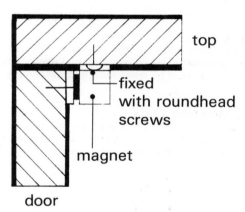

top

fixed
with roundhead
screws

magnet

door

THE PLASTIC 'ROCKER' CATCH

The spring-load rocker of this catch 'clicks' into position over the striking plate which is fixed to the carcase side.

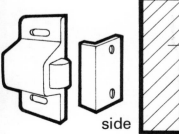

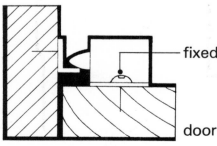

fixed with roundhead screws

side

door

BOLTS AND LOCKS

Bolts can be used on large doors to prevent access from the other side. They are also frequently found in reproduction cabinet work, e.g. kitchen cupboards. They are often made of brass and used as a design feature.

straight bolt with round shoot

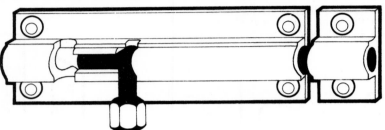

As bolts are made from solid metals, they are very strong, but they are not cheap and are therefore used only for the best work.

Size guide: Bolt lengths are from 50—150 mm.

Locks are for securing a door to prevent access by people other than the keyholder. Each lock has a striking plate which slots into the carcase.

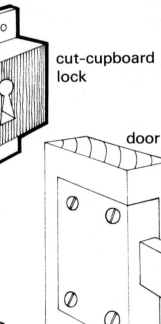

cut-cupboard lock

THE CUT-CUPBOARD LOCK

This lock is recessed into the door edge, giving a neat appearance. It will only turn one way and right- or left-hand must be specified when ordering it.

door

THE MORTISE LOCK

This is the neatest but most expensive lock. It slots into a deep mortise, chopped out of the door edge, and can be operated from either side of the door.

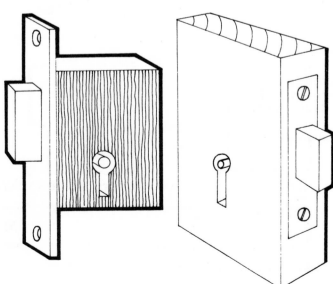

JOINERY FITTINGS

Joinery fittings require strength rather than good looks. They are generally used on softwood jobs and are usually made of steel. The steel is galvanised or black japanned for protection out-doors. Matching screws should be used for fixing these fittings.

THE TEE HINGE

The tapered leaf of the tee hinge supports a door across most of its width and thus prevents sagging. It is commonly used for woodwork bench doors, battened shed doors and light garden gates.
Size guide: Tail length 75—600 mm.

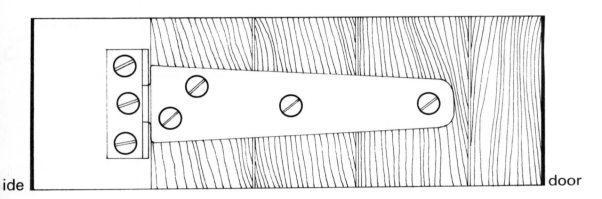

ide · · · door

THE STEP-LADDER HINGE

The illustration shows one of the many types of this hinge. This example is easily fixed, is inexpensive and is safe to use. It opens at a pre-set angle (75°) and locks itself under a heavy load.

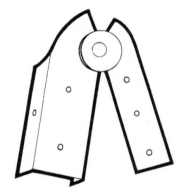

THE HASP AND STAPLE

The light hasp and staple is suitable for securing light doors with a padlock. Larger, heavier versions are made from plate steel. These fold to cover up the fixing screws making them more difficult to unscrew.
Size guide: 60 to 150 mm.

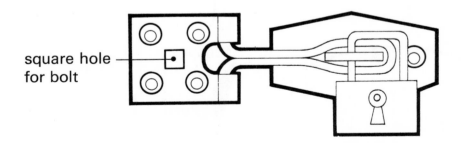

square hole
for bolt

THE TOWER BOLT

The 'shoot' of the tower bolt is held in place by 'saddles' welded to the back 'plate'.
Size guide: 50—300 mm.

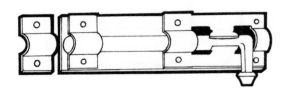

DRAWER FITTINGS

THE DRAWER OR TILL LOCK

This lock is recessed into the edge of the drawer and is not unlike the cut cupboard lock. When fitting such a lock, the body of the lock is recessed off centre to ensure that the keyhole is central on the drawer front.

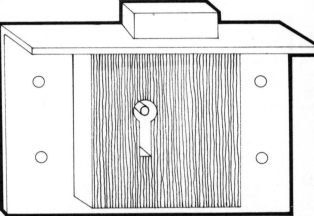

DRAWER HANDLES

Metal, wood, plastic and combinations of these materials are used to make a wide variety of handles.

The **metal handles** in the illustrations have convex and concave knobs. They are attractive to look at and suit modern furniture designs. There are many traditional varieties as well.

Size guide: 22 mm to 38 mm in diameter.

Most metal handles are fixed in a similar way. They are tapped to receive a screw which is passed through the thickness of the drawer front.

The **metal chest handle** is a side-carrying drop handle used on tool boxes etc.

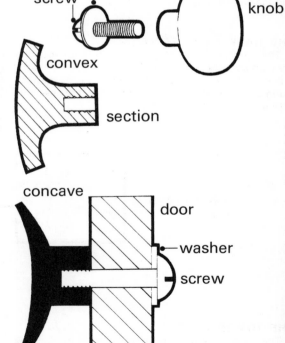

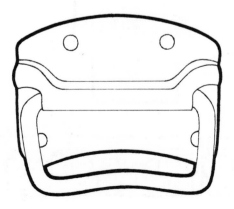

Alloy handles are simple but effective and are often used on kitchen cabinets.

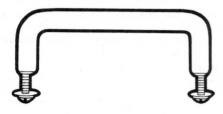

Wood handles can be of almost any timber and shape. Round and square handles are the most usual. The former are turned on a lathe. Square handles are in keeping with the rectangular appearance of many cabinets.

Wood handles and knobs are fixed either by turning to fit a pre-drilled hole or by being screwed through the thickness of the drawer front.

Fixing wood handles

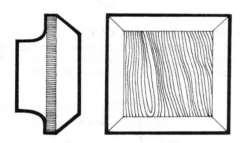

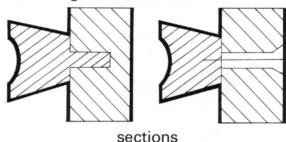

sections

Flexible finger pulls are used in thin sliding doors, e.g. glass, plywood, hardboard.
Size guide: 22 mm and 38 mm diameter.

Manufactured **plastic handles** can be made to almost any shape and in a variety of colours and surface finishes.

BUILT-UP HANDLES

It is often best to design and make up your own handles so that they are in keeping with the remainder of your work. Handles should be considered from the beginning as being an integral part of the design and not as an afterthought to be 'stuck on' at the last moment. Simplicity of design in handles is usually most effective but do not be unwilling to try new ideas.

Built-up handles of contrasting wood/metal combinations can be achieved with proper use of epoxy resins, e.g. *Araldite* or *Britfix*.

Note: Coloured sketches quickly give an impression of the effect your handle will have.

GLASS AND MIRROR FITTINGS

THE MIRROR SCREW

Bathroom mirrors are often predrilled for screwing to the wall. The screw heads may be tapped to allow a chromium-plated cap to cover the screw slot.

THE MIRROR CLIP

Those made from clear plastic are particularly useful for supporting protective glass or perspex over a mounted print. A 12 mm plywood support is ideal.

Use chrome-plated brass clips for heavier mirrors (6 mm thick).

THE GLASS OR MIRROR PLATE

Mirrors held on wood frames are fixed to the wall with a plain or slotted glass plate.
Size guide: Brass or steel 25, 30, 38, 45 mm.

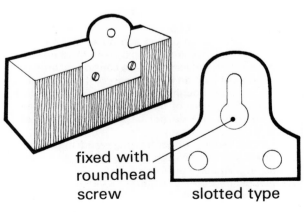

fixed with roundhead screw   slotted type

THE FLUSH MOUNT

These steel fittings are mounted onto the back surface of a framed wall mirror or hanging cabinet and also onto the wall. The object can then be slotted into position and the interlocking tongues ensure a firm joint.

For cleaning and decorating, the mirror or cabinet can be easily detached from the wall.
Size guide: 45 mm × 38 mm.

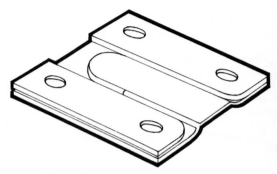

THE PUSH-BUTTON LOCK

A chrome-plated fitting for use on glass sliding doors from 1.5 mm to 9.5 mm thick. The glass must be prepared with a hole 30 mm in diameter.

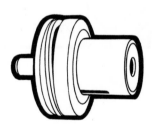

THE GLASS DOOR HINGE

Display cabinets may look elegant with frameless glass doors. The nickel-plated glass door hinge is screwed to the cabinet side and the glass support is covered with a satin-chrome cover plate.
Size guide: Glass 5 to 6 mm thick.

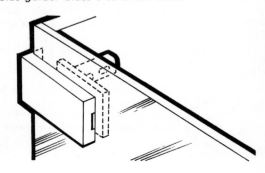

TABLE FITTINGS

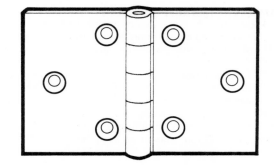

THE BACK FLAP HINGE

This hinge has extra wide leaves which are let into the underside of a table flap.

Size guide: Open sizes in unpolished brass, 25 mm × 38 mm, 32 mm × 49 mm, 38 mm × 58 mm, 51 mm × 78 mm.

THE FOLDING TABLE HINGE

Light tables, such as paperhangers' tables or card tables, may be hinged in the thickness of the top by the folding table hinge.

Size guide: Brass card-table type is 65 mm long.

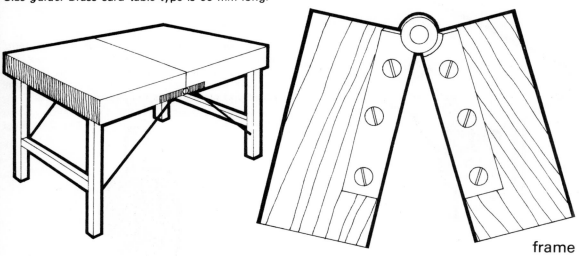

frame

THE TABLE PLATE

Large dining tables can be made to appear light and elegant, yet be sufficiently strong, by using a metal brace fitting.

The dowel screw is driven into the leg and the plate tightened on to it with a wing or standard hexagonal nut.

Size guide: Three sizes to suit different table sizes; 85 mm × 30 mm, 120 mm × 50 mm, 120 mm × 75 mm.

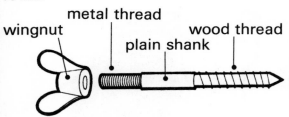

metal thread

wingnut

wood thread

plain shank

FOLDING TABLE FITTING

Tables which are needed occasionally are best designed to fold away when not in use—the classic example being the traditional baize-covered card table.

The bracket designed for this purpose is a steel surface fitting which enables four legs to be attached to the underside of a plain top. Take care to select screws which are strong enough to secure the fitting but which do not project through the top. *Size guide:* 38 mm maximum leg width.

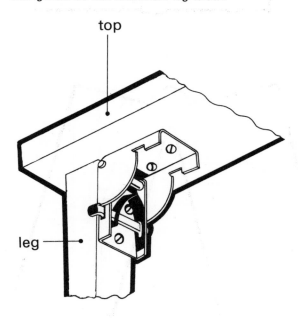

top

leg

THE SLIPPER CASTOR

Where heavy tables or other furniture need to be moved around without damaging the carpet, slipper castors are ideal.

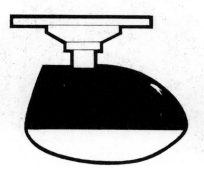

THE REVOLVING CASTOR

A traditional single wheel castor tends to scuff carpets—a problem partly solved by the popular orbital type of fitting.

fixed with roundhead screws

Twin wheel castors are the latest development. They provide a large contact with the floor for stability, make large items easier to move and are available in a variety of attractive colours. Both socket and plate fittings are available.

THE 'RYDERGLYDE'

The coil spring spindle of this castor acts as a brake when pressure is applied to the furniture making it suitable for chairs, settees and beds.

Set with a wider gap, items such as tea trolleys can be 'free rolling' at all times whilst a small gap allows movement only when the furniture is lifted—ideal for tables and filing cabinets.

CARCASE AND BOX FITTINGS

THE PIANO HINGE

This is a continuous strip of hinge made in a variety of metal finishes and also in plastic. It is often used with manufactured slab doors and flaps. It can be cut to any length with a hacksaw. The full-length hinge requires no recessing and the numerous fixing points allow normal screws to be used with veneered chipboard.

THE BOX LOCK

The lock is recessed into the edge of the box and the lid-plate is recessed into the edge of the box lid.
Size guide: 50 mm and 65 mm.

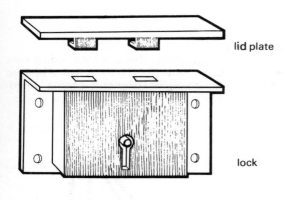

lid plate

lock

STAYS

Stays are made in a variety of finishes, such as chromium, brass and bronze, to suit all types of work.

The joint stay is for limiting the opening of box lids and is generally used on light work.
Size guide: 110 mm, 150 mm and 225 mm.

The silent stay is a long stay used to support the fall flaps of writing and cocktail cabinets. It is made of brass with a nylon slide.
Size guide: 210 mm, 250 mm and 300 mm.

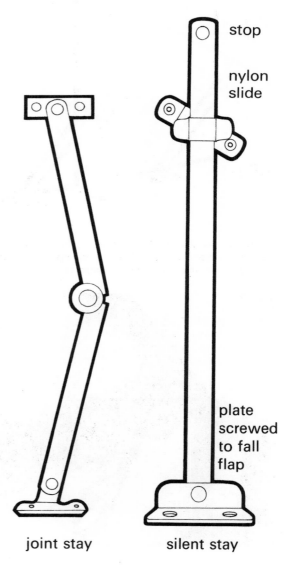

stop

nylon slide

plate screwed to fall flap

joint stay   silent stay

On *modern stays* the speed at which a flap or lid falls can be adjusted by a plastic screw. This is tightened to brake the nickel-plated steel stay as it slides through the plastic fitting.

The double arm stay is the strongest design and is particularly suitable for use on writing desks where the flap may be heavily leaned on. Specify whether you want left or right hand fittings.

Left: Single arm stay.
Size guide: inner lid 300 to 400 mm.
Right: Double arm stay.
Size guide: inner lid more than 405 mm.

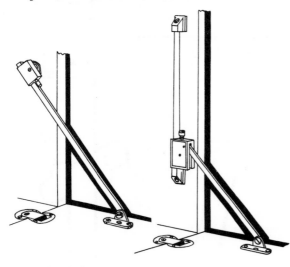

The cam-action locking stay is a heavier fitting which automatically holds the lid in the open position. It's most effective use is on tool chests.

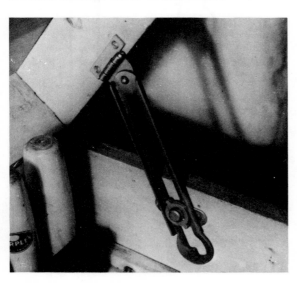

TOP-BOX STAY

Modern wardrobes are often designed with a fairly low hanging rail which leaves room for a 'top-box' for storage. This stay will freely support the flap when it is fully open. Each stay can be adapted for left or right hand fitting.

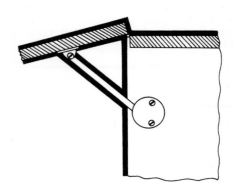

HI-FI STAY

Expensive recording and playback equipment must be properly cared for. This stay has a braking action which controls the lid when it is being closed.

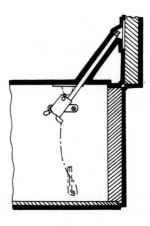

Important. These stays must be properly fitted. Follow the manufacturer's instructions.

INTERIOR FITTINGS

Below are five useful fittings for hanging and holding objects in cabinets and boxes.

The shouldered square hook

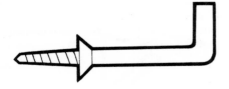

The shouldered cup hook

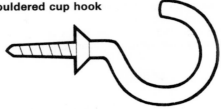

The spring steel clip

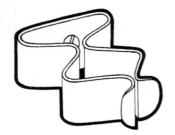

The wardrobe rail centre support (16 and 19 mm diameter)

WALL FITTINGS FOR SOLID WALLS

Mirrors, cabinets, battens etc. may be secured to almost any wall, provided that the correct fitting is used.

Holes in solid walls are drilled with a hand drill or a power unit with a tungsten carbide-tipped drill. Firm pressure must be applied to keep the drill cutting, and power units should be set at a low speed.

All types of masonry can be drilled but if flint or pebble in concrete are likely to cause an obstruction, then a *Rawldrill* must be used. The Rawldrill is hit with a hammer and is turned between blows to produce a neat, round hole.

The Invis socket

plastic covered
steel wardrobe rail

Note: The examples which follow are taken from the Rawlplug range but similar types are available from other manufacturers.

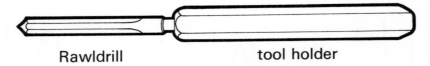

Rawldrill   tool holder

THE RAWLPLUG

Rawlplugs are used as hole fillers for solid walls. They are made from a water-proofed, fibrous material which expands when the screw is inserted. It is important to choose the correct Rawlplug for the screw to be used, so follow the manufacturer's instructions.

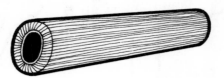

The unthreaded shank should never be forced into the Rawlplug. The joint will not tighten and the wall surface may be damaged. When fixing to plaster walls, the plug should be inserted below the surface to avoid damage when the plug expands.

Note: For easy reference, a number 10 Rawlplug requires a number 10 Rawltool or drill and a number 10 screw.

An alternative to fibre plugs is a plastic tubing which can be cut to the desired length.

THE DELTA SPIRAL NYLON PLUG

This is another hole filler for solid walls. It is used for fixing objects to lightweight building blocks, which are being increasingly used in modern houses.

It has the following features:

An accurate lead-in of screw.

An all-round grip.

It accommodates a plain shank.

It will accept more than one screw size.

Extended fins prevent the plug from turning as the screw is driven home.

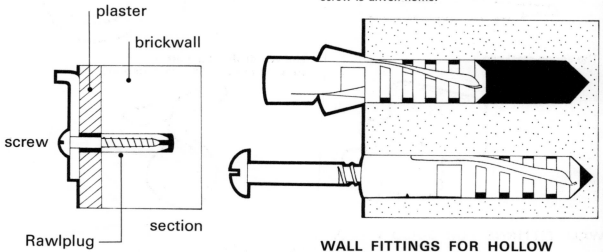

WALL FITTINGS FOR HOLLOW WALLS

THE HARDENED FIXING PIN

These pins are the simplest method of fixing battens to brickwork or breeze block. They must be hit squarely with a succession of light blows to lessen the danger of the nail snapping. (See *Woodwork 1, Section 32*)

Some houses have internal frame walls with a plaster board surface. In these 'hollow' walls, where there is no access to the reverse side, several types of screw-fixing can be used. These include **spring toggles**, **gravity toggles** and **Rawlanchors**.

THE RAWLANCHOR

This is suitable for all hard or soft wall panels. The Rawlanchor is inserted in the hole and when the screw is turned, the anchor collapses.

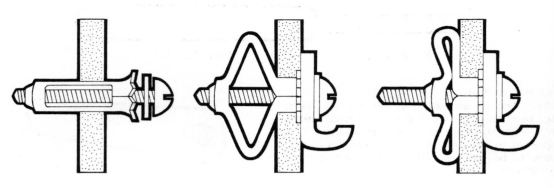

FITTING A BUTT HINGE

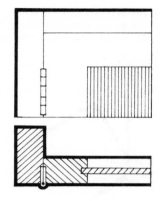

On most cabinet doors two hinges are used and are fixed to the door stile between the top and bottom rails.

The hinge is usually recessed into both the carcase side and the door stile—an equal amount is cut from both.

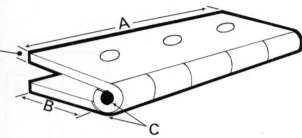

There are four important measurements to consider when fitting the butt hinge:

(a) The length of the hinge.

(b) Half the full hinge width—to the centre of the knuckle.

(c) Half the thickness of the knuckle.

(d) The thickness of the leaf which governs the depth of the recess.

STEPS IN FITTING THE HINGE

(1) Set out the position of the hinge.

(2) Saw across the grain to the hinge length.

(3) Make further saw cuts or cut across the grain using a firmer chisel and mallet.

(4) Remove waste down to the gauge line. Cramp a support in place to prevent the back wall breaking out.

(5) Use a large chisel (hand-pressure only) to ensure that there is a neat back wall to the recess.

(6) Repeat the process on the carcase side, then fix the hinges with one screw and test.

Make any necessary adjustments before final assembly.

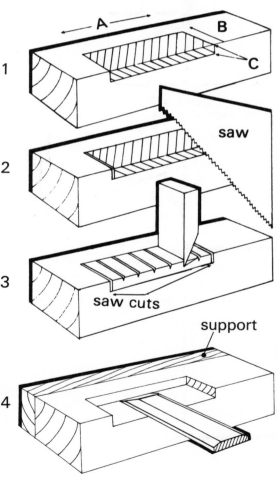

FAULTS TO AVOID:

Recess cut too deep. This strains the hinges and prevents the door from closing. The door is then 'hinge bound'.

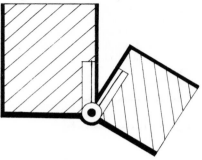

Recess cut too shallow. This leaves an unsightly gap between the door and the carcase.

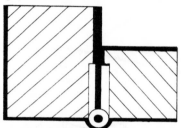

Projecting Screw Heads. This is a common fault. Screws must be of the correct gauge and properly countersunk.

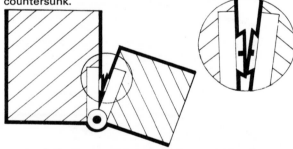

Hinge recessed beyond the centre pin. The carcase will interfere with the door, preventing it from opening fully.

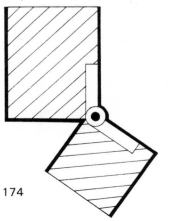

EXAMINATION QUESTIONS

HARDWARE

1. Sketch:
(a) a butt hinge,
(b) a back flap hinge. (S)
2. What type of hinge would you use to hang a light, battened door made of softwood? (N)
3. Describe the purpose for which each of the following is used and illustrate your answer with sketches: slip bolt, ball catch, tee hinge. (JMB)
4. With sketches and notes, show how you would fasten a small hat and coat rack to a brick wall.
5. Name the fittings shown below and state what each is used for.

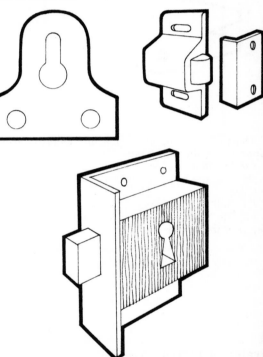

6. You are required to fit the fall flap to the kitchen serving hatch shown below. Explain with the aid of diagrams how to fit: *(a)* the hinges; *(b)* a flap support; *(c)* a catch.

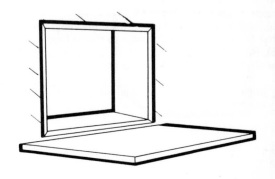

7. With the use of sketches, show in full detail how to fit a butt hinge. List all the tools involved, stating the types of screws used and why. What do you understand by the term 'hingebound' and what causes this?

8. The cupboard door shown is to be hung by means of two 50 mm brass butt hinges. Give step-by-step instructions, with illustrations, for hinging the door.

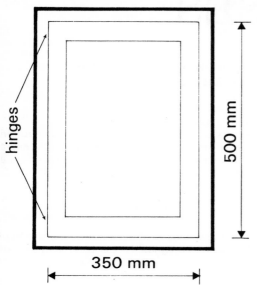

hinges

500 mm

350 mm

9. Sketch and describe how you would fit: (a) a catch suitable for fastening a small cabinet door; (b) a surface bolt on the inside of a pair of doors; (c) a stay to hold a desk fall in the horizontal position.

10. The cabinet shown below is to be made from mahogany. It is to have sliding glass doors above the shelf, and a pair of butt hinged doors below the shelf.

(a) Describe how you would hang one of the hinged doors.
(b) Name and sketch any other fittings you would add to the doors of the cabinet. Describe how you would fit this hardware.
(c) Describe how you would make the grooves for the glass in the two pieces of the cabinet marked A and B.

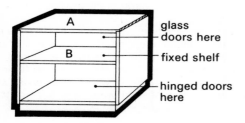

A

B

glass doors here

fixed shelf

hinged doors here

11. The diagram below shows a bathroom cabinet fitted with a plywood back.

(a) Draw the fitting you would use to support an adjustable glass shelf at **A**.
(b) Indicate the position of the door hinges and state their type and material.
(c) Show where you would position the door knobs.
(d) Draw the fitting used to fix the mirrors onto each door.

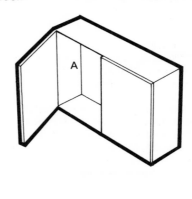

A

12. Hardware fittings made of steel are given a variety of finishes, such as nickel and zinc, bronze and brass plating. Stainless steel and solid brassware are usually self-coloured.

List the fittings used in question 10 and 11 on this page, choose a finish for each and explain each choice.

13. Name the fitment below and state where you would use each part. (W)

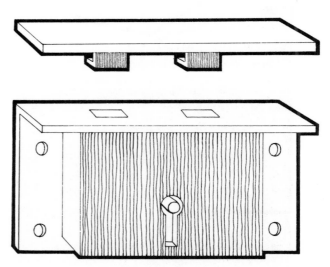

12 NEW MATERIALS, TOOLS AND PROCESSES

INTRODUCTION

Some of the new materials and tools shown in this chapter are already in regular use and many have now become an integral part of workshop equipment and practice.

Self-adhesive veneers, 'throw-away' plane blades and non-stick saws are successful recent developments which confirm that some of the more traditional methods of woodworking and aspects of tool design will soon become a part of craft history. In most cases these new techniques will make our work easier and give us increased scope in the design of furniture.

NEW SURFACE AND EDGE TREATMENTS

PLASTIC LAMINATE

You are already familiar with surfaces covered with plastic sheet, e.g. *Formica*, *Warerite* etc. They are surface veneers with exceptional qualities which are proving invaluable in furniture design.

The laminates are available in many forms:
Single or double sided
Thick or thin (4 mm—1·5 mm)
Postforming (flexible)

Their basic construction is similar, consisting of a core of resin-impregnated paper covered by a decorative sheet which is protected by a transparent sheet.

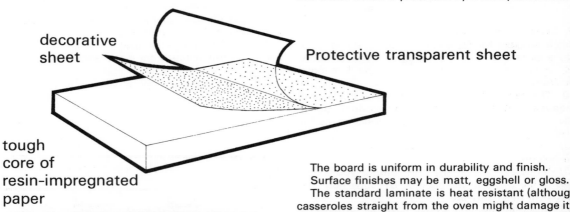

decorative sheet

Protective transparent sheet

tough core of resin-impregnated paper

The board is uniform in durability and finish.

Surface finishes may be matt, eggshell or gloss.

The standard laminate is heat resistant (although casseroles straight from the oven might damage it).

The board remains unmarked by hot water, alcohol or weak acid (vinegar).

It is unlikely to crack or craze in extremely cold or hot conditions.

It is easy to maintain and therefore hygienic. To clean, wipe with a damp cloth or soap and warm water.

An infinite variety of decorative sheets are available. The manufacturers offer a wide range of patterns and colours including realistic woodgrain and marble effects. They have their place in furniture units designed for surfaces which must take a considerable amount of hard wear, e.g. kitchen tops, nursery table tops, bar tops.

CUTTING PLASTIC LAMINATES

Cutting is done with a fine-toothed back saw or sheet saw, which cuts at a low angle. Because the laminate is brittle, it must be well supported to prevent splitting.

Curved shapes may be cut with a coping saw on a V-board, cutting on the downward stroke.

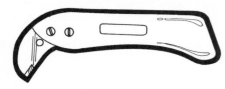

The hard plastic laminate can also be cut with a tungsten carbide tipped cutter such as the Cintride. The photograph shows a similar cutter in use.

A straight edge is held firmly on the top surface of the sheet of laminate and the cutter is drawn across it several times until the top surface is cut through.

Still holding the straight edge in position, the laminate is lifted to break the sheet cleanly along the cut.

BORING PLASTIC LAMINATES

Plastic laminates will quickly blunt saw-tooth boring tools. This tungsten carbide tipped tool can be adjusted to cut holes from 25 mm to 100 mm in diameter and is designed to fit a joiner's handbrace.

THE 'GOSCUT'

Unlike conventional shears, which would bend plastic laminate and crack it, the *Goscut* is designed to support the sheet material at both sides of the cut. There are three interchangeable colour-coded blades. The red blade is specially for plastic laminates, the heavy yellow blade for soft metals and the narrower blue blade for cutting curves in both materials. Each finely-toothed blade removes a strip of material equal to the blade thickness.

PLANING PLASTIC LAMINATES

Edges can be trimmed with a block plane, a *Planemaster*, a *Filemaster* or *Surform*. For a smooth finish, use a fine file or scraper.

The *Cintride* hand sander uses a flexible metal sheet covered in fine tungsten-carbide grit. The finest of the three available grades gives the smoothest possible finish to a laminate edge.

EDGE TREATMENT

This can be done in a variety of materials—matching plastic usually being the most suitable (See *p. 59.*)

Where sheets are to be joined, plastic or aluminium cover strips can be used, and free edges may be protected with an edging or capping.

sections   plastic cap

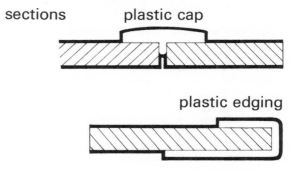

plastic edging

WOOD VENEERS

Considerable difficulty can be experienced when laying wood veneers by traditional methods.

Products such as iron-on veneer and flexible veneer present fewer problems but are more expensive.

IRON-ON VENEER

This veneer is available in fault-free sheets, each coated with a strong adhesive backing. It can be cut with scissors to fit any shape and is applied with a domestic iron. The heat melts the glue which sets on cooling. The surface is pre-sealed and can be given a variety of finishes. Edges can be finished with iron-on matching strips. Timbers available are: Sapele and Teak.

FLEXIBLE VENEER

This is a fairly heavy veneer sandwiched between a layer of aluminium foil and a thick protective layer of clear vinyl. The veneer can be applied with a contact adhesive to blockboard or plywood bases for use as table tops. The surface needs no extra protection as the vinyl will resist heat, even a lighted cigarette, stains, and water. It is cleaned with soap and water.

Edges can be finished with a veneer strip or lipped before the surface veneer is applied.

Sheets are available in Teak, Obechi, Mahogany, Light Oak and Afrormosia.

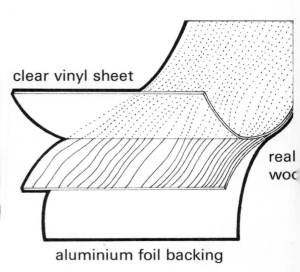

clear vinyl sheet

real woo

aluminium foil backing

ADHESIVES

Contact or impact adhesives are generally used to stick plastic laminates to a manufactured board base. They do this job well, but, besides being messy to apply, they give off a heavy petroleum vapour and are highly inflammable.

Evostick 'non-flam' is a contact adhesive which looks like and is applied in a similar way to PVA glue yet has the advantage of being suitable for bonding polystyrene based plastics.

Application

Apply an even coat of adhesive, using a brush or roller, to both surfaces to be bonded. Do *not* use a 'comb' spreader.

Allow the adhesive to dry.

When the glue changes from its white colour and becomes clear (in about half an hour) the two surfaces should be brought together to form the bond. Sufficient pressure can then be applied with a hand roller.

Care of brushes. Wash in warm water and detergent *immediately* after use.

178

PLANES

The design of such planes as the *Paramo Plane-master* and the *Stanley RBIO* is quite different from that of the traditional metal smoothing and jack plane. This new type of plane has the following features:

The blades are narrow strips of hollow-ground tungsten steel which are cheap and easy to replace, can be sharpened and re-used and can cut brittle laminates.

A rebating attachment may be screwed to either side, making use of the full-width blade.

These planes are also very versatile. A blade used for removing waste wood can quickly be replaced by one for finishing a surface.

Note: Remove corners of blade to prevent 'digging in'.

They are lighter to use than other metal planes and the adjustments are easy to reach and positive to use.

A rigid cutter clamp eliminates chatter and the open sides prevent shavings from choking the mouth.

There is no depth stop or spur when rebating so that in use the depth of cut should be clearly gauged. Across end grain, it would be necessary to saw down the grain before cutting. The accurately ground blades and positive setting help to produce a perfectly square rebate.

Above, right, the 'Planemaster' being used with the detachable fence to cut a rebate.
Below, right, the replaceable blade being slotted into the Stanley RB10.

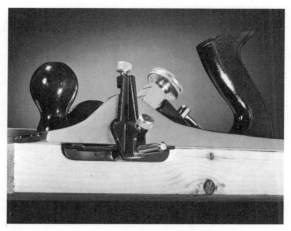

APPLIANCES

The *Copydex Jointmaster* is a sawing jig on which can be cut many familiar joints, including the housing, tenon, halving, dovetail and mitre. A tenon saw is used between two guides and the piece of wood to be sawn positioned accordingly.

In addition to 45° and 90° wood can be cut at five other pre-set angles. A length stop, which allows for the width of the saw cut, and a depth stop make it possible to produce accurate work.

It takes time and care to set up any jig, so you might find it most useful when many identical joints have to be cut. *A jig is not a substitute for skill*.

HOLDING TOOLS

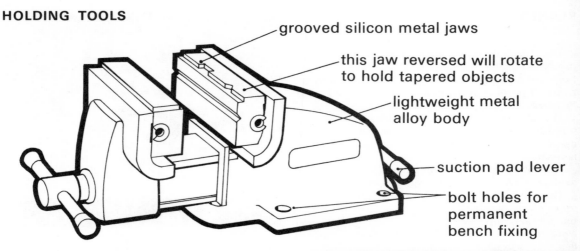

grooved silicon metal jaws

this jaw reversed will rotate to hold tapered objects

lightweight metal alloy body

suction pad lever

bolt holes for permanent bench fixing

THE 'LOCKJAW'

Most portable vices are limited in their use. The *Spear and Jackson Lockjaw* vice performs most of the functions needed by craftsmen working in metal and plastics and is a useful aid to the woodworker. The 100 mm wide jaws only open to 80 mm but with three alternative fixings it is genuinely portable.

The grooved metal jaws provide a secure grip on most sections of material including dowel rod. These can be simply replaced with rubber-faced jaws which will not scratch plastic or plated metal fittings.

Note: Do not use the vice as an anvil.

Above right: A suction pad enables the vice to be used on the flat smooth top of a kitchen table. A G-cramp is supplied to secure it to surfaces up to 60 mm thick (below).

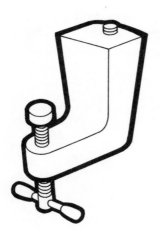

Above: One jaw is reversed so that it pivots to firmly hold the tapered leg.
Below: The grooved rubber jaws hold this chromium-plated handle without damaging the surface.

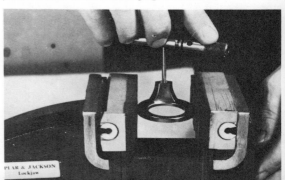

THE 'JET CLAMP'

The *Jet Clamp* is one of a new generation of holding devices which will do many of the jobs formerly done by the traditional G-cramp and heavy sash cramp.

Interchangeable circular pads with a smooth or serrated metal surface, soft neoprene and edge location pads can be fitted into the swivel brackets. Four lengths of bar are available (305 mm, 610 mm, 915 mm and 1220 mm) which can be fitted with more than one pair of arms. These arms can be positioned anywhere on the bar and the grip is provided by the action of a spring loaded jamming wedge, moved into action by turning the tightening bar.

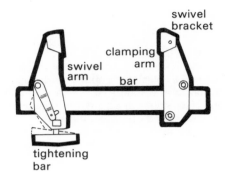

Above: The edge cramp locating pads prevent the clamps from slipping off square edged boards and frames.

Below: The soft neoprene pads protect the surface of wood which has been 'finished' whilst a moulding is cut.

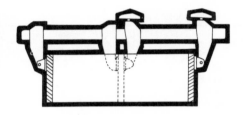

Above: Where a fixed shelf in pre-veneered chipboard is being pinned or screwed in position, two pairs of arms mounted on one bar will hold it in position.

Below: The clamp arms are used in reverse to push apart a dry-jointed frame.

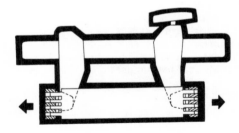

NOTES TO STUDENTS

WRITING A STUDY

Many examining boards require a study or project to be completed as part of the craft course work. The idea of planning and writing a study is to give you an opportunity of exploring an aspect of woodwork in which you may have a particular interest.

The following notes are a practical guide to your choice of a topic, the presentation of your work, and possible sources of information.

For course work, it is usually possible to choose almost any subject loosely connected with woodwork. You will produce the best work by writing about your own particular interest, but understandably, some of you will find it difficult to select a suitable topic. Discuss the problem with your teacher. Choose a subject which has limits. 'Trees', for example, is a vague subject on which you are likely to write (and copy) too much. On the other hand, the title, 'British Trees', or even 'British Hardwoods', would give you plenty of scope to plan an acceptable study within defined limits.

The titles listed below have formed the basis of course work for pupils taking C.S.E. examinations. The list gives an indication of the range of subjects that can be studied.

STUDY TITLES

Wood
Tropical Trees
British Trees
The Destruction and Restoration of Forests
Trees in the School Grounds
The Importance of Man-Made Boards
Plywood
The Deterioration of Timber
Wood Finishing
Insect Attack on Hardwoods
Timber Preservatives
Some Experiments on Wood Finishes

Uses of Wood
Timber in Aircraft Design
Uses of British Hardwoods
Building Timber
Wood in Metal Ships
Wood for Musical Instruments
Gun Stocks
Paper Production

Tools
Cramping Devices
The Hand Saw
Forestry Saws
Machine Saws — a Survey
Home-made Jigs and Templates
How a Chisel is Made
Blades — Their Uses and Importance

Construction
Selecting Adhesives
A History of Glues
Wood Joints Used in the Furniture Industry
Building a Pram Dinghy

Fitting out a Kitchen
Ship Building
Making a Coffee Table

Crafts
The Windsor Chair Maker
The Wheelwright
The Village Blacksmith
A Local Craftsman
Austrian Wood Carving
Wood Turning
A Career in Forestry
A Joiner's Apprentice

Design
Tables — a Survey of Modern Designs
School Furniture
Garden Carpentry
A Survey of Garden Furniture in Shops
Church Roof Design
Furniture to Keep Things In
Modern Guitars
Wood Handles

History
Thomas Sheraton
The Furniture Makers
20th-Century Craftsmen
A History of Chairs
Chests and Commodes
The Age of Oak
The Story of Furniture
A History of Bench Planes
The Development of the Wood Lathe
A History of the House
Caravan Development

PRESENTATION OF THE PROJECT

This will vary according to the instructions you receive but the following suggestions might be considered.

The work will be done over a period of several months and it is best to keep your notes in a loose-leaf file or ring-folder.

Ring-folders are also ideal bindings for the presentation of the finished study.

A typed script is easier to read than handwriting and the assessor of the study will certainly appreciate it if you are able to have your work typed. Try the 'Commerce Department' of a school. Some student may be persuaded to show off her typing skill—for a small token of appreciation. Ask for a carbon copy as well. Your teacher may like to put a copy in his 'library'. The text should be typed on one side of the sheet only and should be in double spacing with generous margins.

Standardise the headings throughout the study and number each page, drawing and photograph clearly, when the study is finished.

Keep your drawings and photographs next to the relevant text.

Aim to produce a high standard in the illustrations, which should be clearly labelled.

The use of rub-on display lettering such as *Letraset* or *Blick* will make this task easier and improve the appearance of the work.

After numbering the pages, make out a list of contents (with page references) for the front of the study, and design a suitable 'Title Page'.

The study must include an acknowledgment to firms and/or individuals who have supplied you with information. It should conclude with a bibliography, i.e. a list of the books to which you have referred.

Samples of thin materials, e.g. upholstery cloth, can often be stuck on to pages of the study. Wood samples and the like, cut to a standard size and boxed or mounted on a small display board, also add interest. They must be clearly and accurately labelled in relation to the text.

SOURCES OF INFORMATION

The title 'study' indicates that you are not expected to contribute an outstanding piece of original writing on a particular topic, nor are you expected to copy large sections from another book or leaflet. Copied work is usually obvious to the assessor and he will not assess it very highly. You *are* expected to go to sources of reference and gather together information related to your subject and then present it in a clear and logical way. Read widely, make notes and then write down the information in your own words. Your school and local libraries will be your main sources of information.

Note: The librarian will not be pleased if you trace drawings from a book because it will damage the page. Make a sketch copy of any illustration you want to use.

See pp. 184–6 for other sources of information.

REQUEST FOR INFORMATION

The letter below is an example of how you would request information in a clear and courteous manner.

11 South Road,
Northwich,
Hampshire.

22nd October 1980

The Publicity Manager,
Spear & Jackson (Tools) Ltd.,
St Paul's Road,
Wednesbury,
Staffordshire,
WS10 9RA

Dear Sir,

I am making a study of 'New Materials in Tool Manufacture' as part of my course work for the Certificate of Secondary Education in Woodwork.

I should be grateful to receive illustrated information on your full range of handsaws, particularly those with the recently developed plastic handles.

Yours faithfully,

(Your signature)

INFORMATION FROM FIRMS AND ORGANISATIONS

Some small firms, with a minimum number of clerical staff, are not in a position to give information to thousands of enquiring pupils. The firms listed below, however, are willing to supply a variety of specific information for a particular study, free of charge, although in some instances, a large stamped addressed envelope is required.

ADDRESSES FOR REFERENCE

Timber Research

Head of Laboratory,
Building Research Establishment,
Princes Risborough Laboratory,
Princes Risborough,
AYLESBURY
Bucks HP17 9PX

No envelope

UAC Timber,
P.O. Box 1,
Blackfriars Road,
LONDON SE1 9UG

No envelope

Manufactured Constructional Material

The Education Officer,
FIDOR (The Fibre Building Board Development Organisation Limited)
Buckingham House,
6/7 Buckingham Street,
LONDON WC2N 6BZ

No envelope

Berman Bros. (Panels) Ltd.,
Goodwin Road,
Edmonton,
LONDON N9 0EP

No envelope

P.R. Dept.,
Formica Limited,
84/86 Regent Street,
LONDON W1A 1DL

No envelope

Hand Tools

James Neill (Sheffield) Ltd.,
Napier Street,
SHEFFIELD, S.11 8HB
Yorks.

No envelope

The Sales Promotion Department,
Firth Brown Tools Ltd.,
Speedicut Works,
Carlisle Street East,
P.O. Box 59,
SHEFFIELD S4 7QP

No envelope

Thor Hammer Co. Ltd.,
Highlands Road,
SHIRLEY
Nr Birmingham B90 4NJ

No envelope

Alec Tiranti Ltd.,
70, High Street,
THEALE
Berkshire

No envelope

The Publicity Manager,
F. Parramore & Sons, (1924) Ltd.,
Caledonian Works,
Chapeltown,
SHEFFIELD, S.30 4WZ
Yorks.

Stamped addressed envelope (s.a.e.)

**Vices, Planes, Cramps,
Chisels and Boring Tools**

Educational Adviser,
Record Ridgway Tools Ltd.,
Parkway Works,
SHEFFIELD S9 3BL

s.a.e

Saws and Vices

The Publicity Manager,
Spear and Jackson Ltd.,
St Paul's Road,
WEDNESBURY
Staffordshire WS10 9RA

No envelope

**Hammers, Planes, Screwdrivers,
Braces, Drills and Measuring
Tools**

Stanley Education Service,
Stanley Tools Ltd.,
Woodside,
SHEFFIELD, S.3 9PD
Yorks.

No envelope

**Abrasives, Masonry Drills,
Glass Drills and Tile Cutters**

Cintride Limited,
Grange Lane Works,
SHEFFIELD, S.5 ODR

No envelope

The Personnel and Training Officer,
The English Abrasives Corporation Ltd.,
Marsh Lane,
Tottenham,
LONDON, N. 17

No envelope

The Carborundum Company Ltd.,
Coated Abrasives Division,
P.O. Box 60,
ACCRINGTON
Lancashire BB5 5JN

s.a.e.

Power Tools Ltd.,
Cliff Works,
Vernon Road,
SCARBOROUGH
Yorkshire

s.a.e.

Machine Tools and Safety

E.P. Barrus Ltd.,
Brunel Road,
Acton,
LONDON W3 7UY

s.a.e

Denford Machine Tools Ltd.,
Birds Royd,
BRIGHOUSE
Yorkshire HD6 1NB

No envelope

T. S. Harrison and Sons Ltd.,
Union Street,
HECKMONDWIKE
West Yorkshire WF16 0HN

s.a.e.

Safety Products Ltd.,
Holmethorpe Avenue,
REDHILL
Surrey RH1 2PA

s.a.e.

Stanley-Bridges Ltd.,
Nelson Way,
CRAMLINGTON
Northumberland NE23 9JS

No envelope

Timber Preservative and Finishing

The Publicity Department,
Cuprinol Ltd.,
Preservation Centre,
5, Stag Place,
LONDON SW1E 5AP

No envelope

Rentokil Advice Centre,
16, Dover Street,
LONDON W1X 4DJ

s.a.e.

Wood Dyes, Seals and Polishes

Rustins Ltd.,
Waterloo Road,
Cricklewood,
LONDON NW2 7TX

s.a.e.

Sterling Roncraft,
Chapeltown,
SHEFFIELD S30 4YP

s.a.e.

Adhesives

Ciba-Greigy (UK) Ltd.,
Plastics Division,
Duxford,
CAMBRIDGE CB2 4QA.

No envelope

The Sales Office,
Evode Ltd.,
Common Road,
STAFFORD ST16 3EH

No envelope

Unibond Ltd.,
Industrial Estate,
CAMBERLEY
Surrey

s.a.e.

Hardware

The Sales Department,
James Collins (B'ham) Ltd.,
Salford Street,
Long Acre,
BIRMINGHAM B6 7SG

No envelope

Isaac Lord Ltd.,
Desborough Road,
HIGH WYCOMBE
Bucks. HP11 2QN

s.a.e.

Home Consultant,
Swish Products Ltd.,
TAMWORTH
Staffs. B79 7TW

No envelope

Fixing Devices and Tools

The Sales Promotion Department,
The Rawlplug Company Ltd.,
147, London Road,
KINGSTON-UPON-THAMES,
Surrey.

No envelope

Upholstery

The Customer Service Dept.,
Riveting Systems Ltd.,
Harehill,
TODMORDEN
Lancs. OL14 5JY

No envelope

Sewing Advisory Service,
English Sewing Ltd.,
56, Oxford Street,
MANCHESTER M60 1HJ

No envelope

Pirelli Ltd.,
Derby Road,
BURTON ON TRENT
Staffs. DE13 0BH

No envelope

Selectus Ltd.,
Biddulph,
STOKE ON TRENT ST8 7RH

s.a.e.